Just for the Fun of It!

A Collection of AIMS Mathematical Investigations

Authors
Dave Youngs

Michelle Youngs

Editor
Betty Cordel

Illustrator
Brenda Richmond

Desktop Publisher
Tracey Lieder

© 1999 AIMS Education Foundation

This book contains materials developed by the AIMS Education Foundation. **AIMS** (**A**ctivities **I**ntegrating **M**athematics and **S**cience) began in 1981 with a grant from the National Science Foundation. The non-profit AIMS Education Foundation publishes hands-on instructional materials (books and the monthly magazine) that integrate curricular disciplines such as mathematics, science, language arts, and social studies. The Foundation sponsors a national program of professional development through which educators may gain both an understanding of the AIMS philosophy and expertise in teaching by integrated, hands-on methods.

ISBN **1-881431-79-7**

Printed in the United States of America

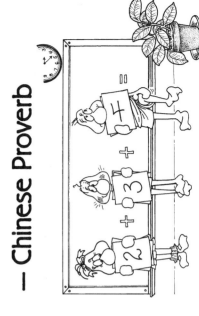

I Hear and I Forget,

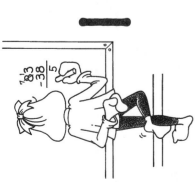

I See and I Remember,

I Do and I Understand.

— Chinese Proverb

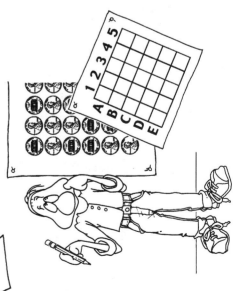

Table Of Contents

Introduction

Just For the Fun of It! is a collection of open-ended mathematical investigations for students in grades four through eight. These investigations were written with three goals in mind: 1) to foster positive feelings about mathematics by introducing teachers and students to the fascinating world of recreational mathematics—doing math just for the fun of it!; 2) to embody the curriculum and evaluation standards from the National Council of Teachers of Mathematics (NCTM); and 3) to provide teachers with a wide selection of motivating problem-solving investigations for their students.

The major goal of this publication is to introduce you and your students to the wonderful world of recreational mathematics. This tradition goes back thousands of years. (See the *Background Information* section in the first activity for more on this topic.) Unfortunately, this long-standing tradition is absent from many modern classrooms. Mathematics in these classrooms may be viewed as necessary and utilitarian, but certainly not recreational. However, with the proper care and nurturing, a positive—just for the fun of it—attitude can be kindled in students. The investigations presented here are intended to help this happen in your classroom.

Along with building positive attitudes towards mathematics, every one of the investigations in this book gives students the opportunity to experience, firsthand, four of the NCTM's curriculum and evaluation standards: mathematics as problem solving, mathematics as communication, mathematics as reasoning, and mathematical connections. In addition, many of the activities also embody other standards such as patterns and functions, number and number relationships, computation and estimation, probability, algebra, and geometry. When doing the investigations in this book, your students will experience and learn mathematics in the true spirit of the NCTM's standards.

Each of the investigations here is designed in such a way that it can be done as a stand-alone activity with students who have mastered the basic operations of arithmetic. While they are not intended to be done sequentially, the more difficult and/or involved investigations have been placed later in the book and are not recommended until students have had sufficient experience with open-ended problems. The investigations cover a broad range of topics which includes such things as mathematical patterns, paradoxes, and microworlds. Students who actively engage in these investigations will expand their mathematical horizons and improve their problem-solving and divergent-thinking skills.

It is my sincere hope that this book and its investigations will help you and your students embark on a wonderful mathematical journey. As you travel together you can explore the power and beauty of mathematics while simultaneously experiencing doing math just for the fun of it. Bon voyage!

Dave Youngs

Some Suggestions for Using this Book

- **Be enthusiastic and show that you enjoy math**
  If you want students to develop positive attitudes towards mathematics and problem solving, it is critical that you model these same attitudes. If you become excited when students find a new pattern or make some interesting discovery, they will see that you value and enjoy mathematics.

- **Do the problems yourself**
  You can't teach problem solving effectively unless you become a problem solver. Doing each investigation yourself before assigning it to students not only gives you the chance to apply your own problem-solving strategies, it also gives you a clear idea of what your students are asked to do in the investigation. So, please resist the temptation to read the solutions before you've tried the problems.

- **Emphasize the process as well as the product**
  Students often have the mistaken idea that the only important thing in math is to get the right answer. Help dispel this notion by valuing the process of problem solving as much as correct answers.

- **Encourage multiple methods of solution and divergent thinking**
  Every investigation in this book can—and should—be done in multiple ways. Unlike computation, where a single method is often stressed, good problem solving is divergent and open-ended. There is no single "right way" to do any of these problems.

- **Create a classroom problem-solving strategies chart**
  As students gain experience in solving problems, they begin to use strategies other than guess and check. After your students have gained some experience in problem solving, create a classroom problem-solving strategies chart together that lists these strategies. Add to this chart whenever students discover new strategies. Your chart may include such things as looking for patterns, drawing pictures or diagrams, organizing information in tables and charts, working backwards, doing similar simpler problems, and asking insightful questions.

- **Build persistence**
  One of the most important characteristics of a good problem solver is persistence. Students who give up too quickly will never become problem solvers—encourage them to keep trying if they don't find an immediate answer.

- **Explore the problems in depth**
  Many of the investigations in this book lend themselves to in-depth exploration. This type of exploration requires an investment of time, but this investment should prove valuable.

- **Let students make the problem "theirs" by extending it**
  The majority of the problems presented here can be extended quite easily. While each investigation includes suggested extensions, it is always best if the ideas for extensions come from the students. When students think of interesting questions to explore, they make the problem their own. This is exactly what mathematicians do when they explore new problems.

- **Foster collaboration**
  Rather than having students work independently, encourage them to collaborate. Since problem solving is a divergent activity, this allows students to learn from each other as they work together on an investigation.

- **Facilitate—don't tell**
  It may be difficult to do, but try to get students to discover the richness of each problem through their own explorations, not your explanations. This takes practice, but is well worth the effort. For example, a question like, "How might you organize this information to help you solve the problem?" might push students to come up with their own organizational scheme while saying, "Put the numbers in a table according to the following rules...." solves the problem for students and robs them of the chance to find an organizational scheme for themselves.

- **Don't neglect the wrap-up discussions**
  In many instances the most valuable part of an investigation is the discussion at the end where students share their thoughts, discoveries, methods, and solutions. These sessions provide students with the opportunity to communicate mathematically with their peers and with you. This discussion can help students expand their problem-solving repertoires as they learn how others approached the problems. Make sure to leave ample time for this important activity.

A Philosophy of Problem Solving

The cover of this book pictures a Soma Cube being put together. At the base of the cube is the statement: "Problems worthy of attack prove their worth by hitting back." This short poem, called a grook, was written by Piet Hein, the multi-talented inventor of the Soma Cube (see *Cube Construction* for more on Hein). This grook sets the stage for the mathematical investigations you will encounter in this publication—each one should prove a worthy, and worthwhile, challenge for your students, even if they are adept at computation.

Problem solving is usually more difficult for students than computation because it is such a different undertaking. It requires mathematical reasoning rather than rote application of a memorized algorithm. It is also divergent and process oriented rather than convergent and answer oriented. Problem solving encourages multiple methods of solution rather than the single method usually encountered in computation. In addition, proficiency in computation doesn't automatically make students problem solvers.

Because of these differences, it often takes more time for students to build proficiency in problem solving than it does in computation. However, the time invested is well worth it. This is because students use computational skills in a meaningful context when they solve problems, so engaging in problem solving also gives students practice in computation. The reverse, however, is not true—students who only do computation don't get to practice problem solving and build competence in this important life skill.

Building proficiency in problem solving takes time, but then so do most worthwhile endeavors in life. Students can't become problem solvers without continuous exposure to good problems. The following grook by Hein, therefore, is an appropriate reminder as you and your students embark on your problem-solving journey.

T.T.T

Put up in a place
where it's easy to see
the cryptic admonishment
T.T.T.

When you feel how
depressingly slowly you climb,
it's well to remember
Things Take Time.

— Piet Hein

Total Count-Ability

Topic
Divergent thinking, multiple solutions

Key Question
How many different answers can you find and justify for the nursery rhyme *Going to St. Ives*?

Focus
Students will learn that some problems can have multiple solutions depending on how they are interpreted by coming up with at least three possible answers to the nursery rhyme *Going to St. Ives* and justifying each one.

Guiding Document
NCTM Standards
- *Develop and apply a variety of strategies to solve problems, with emphasis on multistep and nonroutine problems*
- *Verify and interpret results with respect to the original problem situation*
- *Justify answers and solution processes*

Math
Whole number operations

Integrated Processes
Observing
Comparing and contrasting

Materials
Student sheet
Calculators, optional

Background Information

> As I was going to St. Ives
> I met a man with seven wives.
> Every wife had seven sacks,
> Every sack had seven cats,
> Every cat had seven kits.
> Kits, cats, sacks and wives,
> How many were going to St. Ives?

This version of the familiar nursery rhyme first appeared in 18th century England, but its roots go back much further than that. A variation appears in Leonardo Fibonacci's *Liber Abaci* from the early 13th century which reads:

> Seven old women are on the road to Rome. Each woman has seven mules,

each mule carries seven sacks, each sack contains seven loaves, with each loaf there are seven knives, and each knife is in seven sheaths. How many objects are there: women, mules, sacks, loaves, knives, sheaths?

Even this version is not the first appearance of this problem. The earliest evidence dates back to ancient Egypt where the Rhind papyrus (originally written c. 1800 BCE) records the solution to an unwritten problem. The solution clearly suggests a form of the St. Ives rhyme:

Houses	7
Cats	49
Mice	343
Sheaves of wheat	2401
Hekats of grain	6807
Total	19607

Dominic Olivastro, in his book *Ancient Puzzles*, conjectures that this list may have been the recording, by the scribe Ahmes, of the answer to a common puzzle of the time. This puzzle may have been as follows: A man owned seven houses. In each house, there were seven cats. Each cat killed seven mice. Each mouse ate seven sheaves of wheat. Each sheaf had seven hekats of grain. Grain, wheat, mice, cats, houses: What was the man's entire estate?

Evidently in ancient times, the problem was presented as an exercise to be solved. This is in contrast to the St. Ives rhyme, which is presented as a trick question. The answer is said to be one, because if the narrator was on his way *to* St. Ives, the man and his wives would have been coming *from* St. Ives (although this is assumed and not explicitly stated), thus only one person is going *to* St. Ives. This modern interpretation greatly limits the scope of the problem. The goal of *Total Count-Ability* is to extend both the modern and ancient perspectives by having students justify multiple solutions to the rhyme (see *Solutions*).

Management
1. Students must think creatively in order to come up with alternate solutions to this problem. Encourage these creative and divergent thinking processes.
2. The use of calculators by students is optional; however, it can save a lot of time and needless error in the computation of the large totals.
3. When students share their solutions, you will want to have a large area where the groups can record

and justify their responses. This might be the chalkboard, a bulletin board or a large piece of butcher paper that everyone can access easily.

Procedure
1. Hand out the student sheet and read the nursery rhyme aloud to the class.
2. Have students work in groups and allow them time to come up with a variety of solutions on their own.
3. After each group has had a chance to come up with at least two different answers, have them share the various solutions and the justifications for those solutions. See if any more solutions can be found as a class.
4. Have each group record a different solution and the justification for it on the chalkboard (bulletin board, butcher paper, etc.).

Discussion
1. The "answer" to this problem according to the traditional interpretation is one. What does this answer assume about the problem? [The man (and his wives) were coming from St. Ives when the narrator met him (them).]
2. What other answers did you come up with?
3. What reasoning did you have to use to come up with those answers?

Extensions
1. Have students find or create other mathematical number rhymes similar to *Going to St. Ives*.
2. For older students this activity can be used as an introduction to, or practice with, exponents. The solutions which involve the wives, sacks, cats and kits are powers of seven, and if recognized as such can open up avenues for further exploration.
3. With older students you may wish to explore the Egyptian numeration system used on the Rhind Papyrus. Egyptians used a *tally numeration system* in which there is a one-to-one correspondence between the tallies and what is being counted. They used specific symbols to represent groupings of numbers and employed an *additive property*, meaning that the value of a number was the sum of the values of the symbols and tally marks. For example, 10 was represented by a heel bone symbol ($\supset$) and 100 was represented by a scroll ($\circlearrowleft$). Symbols were usually written in increasing order, thus ($/ \supset \circlearrowleft \circlearrowleft$) equals 211. Students can use the Egyptian numeration system to solve additional problems, or invent their own system based on the same concept. For further information on the Egyptian numeration system, see *A Problem Solving Approach to Mathematics for Elementary School Teachers,* Sixth Edition by Billstein, Libeskind & Lott (1993). For further information

on the Rhind Papyrus, see *Ancient Puzzles* by Dominic Olivastro (1993).

Solutions
Following are six solutions and their justifications. Your class may think of other possible solutions, and as long as they can be logically justified, they are acceptable.

How many are going to St. Ives?
- One: The narrator was on his way *to* St. Ives and met the man (and his wives) coming *from* St. Ives.
- Two: The narrator met the man on the road to St. Ives and they were both going the same direction. The man told the narrator about his wives and their sacks, but none of them were actually present.
- 2802: The narrator came upon the man and his wives who were traveling to St. Ives slowly, encumbered by their sacks full of cats and kittens. [2 men, 7 wives, 49 sacks, 343 cats, 2401 kits]
- 2753: As above, the narrator came upon the man and his wives, but the sacks are not alive, so why would they be counted? [2 men, 7 wives, 343 cats, 2401 kits]
- Nine: As above, the narrator came upon the man and his wives, but sacks, cats and kits don't matter, only people should be counted. [2 men, 7 wives]
- 2800: The last line of the poem says, "Kits, cats, sacks and wives, how many were going to Ives?" It is not asking about the narrator or the man, merely about the kits, cats, sacks and wives. [7 wives, 49 sacks, 343 cats, 2401 kits]

Total Count-Ability

As I was going to St. Ives,
I met a man with seven wives.
Every wife had seven sacks,
Every sack had seven cats,
Every cat had seven kits,
Kits, cats, sacks and wives,
How many were going to St. Ives?

Read the above poem. How many do you think were going to St. Ives? What assumptions did you make to arrive at this answer? Discuss your answer and assumptions with your group.

As a group, see if you can find at least three possible answers to this poem. Justify each answer and clearly state the assumptions made to arrive at that answer.

Record your answers and assumptions on the back.

The Fascinating Triangle

Topic
Mathematical microworlds

Key Question
How can the numbers one to six be arranged on the sides of a triangle so that each side has the same sum?

Focus
Students will be challenged to ask questions, think mathematically, and see the patterns that exist in the solutions. Older students will also be challenged with informal proofs.

Guiding Documents
Project 2061 Benchmark
- *Mathematics is the study of many kinds of patterns, including numbers and shapes and operations on them. Sometimes patterns are studied because they help to explain how the world works or how to solve practical problems, sometimes because they are interesting in themselves.*

NCTM Standards
- *Reflect on and clarify thinking about mathematical ideas and situations*
- *Justify answers and solution processes*
- *Generalize solutions and strategies to new problem situations*

Math
Whole number operations
Math patterns

Integrated Processes
Observing
Comparing and contrasting
Inferring
Generalizing
Applying

Materials
Student sheets
Number cards (scratch paper or sticky notes)
Scissors, optional

Background Information
In mathematics, a microworld is a mathematical environment which is governed by simple rules and structures. This problem appears at first glance to be a simple arithmetic exercise. However, if it is used properly it can open the doors to a rich mathematical microworld in which students are free to explore, discover, and "do" mathematics.

An important feature of this investigation is the realization that some problems have multiple correct and valid solutions. This realized, the goal changes from finding "the" answer to finding *all* possible answers, and then *asking questions to extend the problem.* One of the things which makes this investigation so rich is that it contains an abundance of patterns. This investigation also encourages students to do higher-level mathematical thinking, which can lead to informal proofs and algebraic reasoning.

Management
1. Students will need to construct the number cards used for this activity. A quarter sheet of scratch paper per student cut into ninths (fold in thirds horizontally and vertically and cut along folds) will make cards of an appropriate size. Have students write the numbers one to nine on the cards, and set aside the seven to nine cards for the time being. An alternative is to use small-sized sticky notes for the number cards.
2. The initial goal of this investigation is for students to discover that it has multiple solutions; this should not be told to them while explaining the procedure.
3. Once students discover that there is more than one solution, the goal becomes for them to discover all four possible sums for the numbers one to six.
4. The whole-class sharing session is the most important part of this activity. During this time the students should share any discoveries and/or patterns they have found. In addition, they should share any questions or ideas they have for extensions. Your facilitation of this discussion is critical. Students should be encouraged to discover as much as they can about this problem during this part of the lesson. Your enthusiasm and encouragement will help students to think mathematically and enjoy their discoveries.

Procedure
1. Have students make their number cards.
2. Hand out the first two student sheets and go over the directions. *Place the number cards one to six in the six spaces so the sums of the three numbers on each side of the triangle are equal.*

4

3. Give students time to come up with all four sums and record them, allowing them to work in groups or by themselves.
4. Be sure that students keep an accurate record of their solutions. This will be essential for them to be able to see the patterns that exist.
5. When students have had sufficient time to discover multiple solutions to the problem, hand out the third student sheet and have the students answer the questions there.
6. Have a time of discussion and group sharing in which students share the patterns they have discovered as well as any insight they have into the problem.
7. Challenge the students to ask questions for further discovery (see *Discussion*). If necessary hand out the optional fourth student sheet to facilitate this process.

Discussion

1. What is the smallest sum possible? [nine] Why? [Since the six must go somewhere, the smallest possible numbers to go with it are one and two, giving a total of nine.]
2. What is the largest sum possible? [12] Why? [Since the one must go somewhere, the largest possible numbers to go with it are six and five, giving a total of 12.]
3. What patterns do you notice in the four different sums? (See *Solutions*.)
4. What happens to the sum when the corners are odd? [The sum is even.]
5. What happens to the sum when the corners are even? [The sum is odd.]
6. What would happen if we used different numbers other than one to six (i.e. two to seven, three to eight, etc.)? [The patterns would continue with different sums.]
7. What sums would you predict? Be specific. [e.g. For two to seven, actual sums are 12, 13, 14, and 15. Predicted sums might be 10, 11, 12, and 13.]
8. Why are the sums for two to seven three more than the sums for one to six? [When you increase the sequence by one, the value of each number increases by one (one becomes two, two becomes three, three becomes four, etc.). Since you are adding three numbers on each side of the triangle, you increase the sums by a total of three instead of just one. For example, the largest sum possible for one to six is 12 (1 + 5 + 6), while the smallest sum possible for two to seven is 12 (2 + 3 + 7).]
9. What would the sums for three to eight be? [15, 16, 17, 18] Why? [3 + 4 + 8 = 15, 3 + 7 + 8 = 18]

Extensions

Ideally these extensions will arise from the questions the students pose during the sharing session. If not,

you may prompt them to get them thinking along the right track, and then see what they come up with.
1. Use the numbers two to seven, three to eight, four to nine, etc.
2. Use consecutive odd numbers (1, 3, 5, 7, 9, 11, etc.).
3. Use consecutive even numbers (2, 4, 6, 8, 10, 12, etc.).
4. Use numbers which have a common difference (e.g., 2, 5, 8, 11, 14, 17; difference = 3).
5. Use prime numbers (e.g., 2, 3, 5, 7, 11, 13)
6. Use fractions instead of whole numbers (e.g., 1/6, 2/6, 3/6, 4/6, 5/6, 6/6). The fractions used must consist of regularly constructed multiples, have a regular interval, or consist of a combination of the above. For students used to working with uncommon denominators, reduced equivalents can be used (1/8, 1/4, 3/8, 1/2, 5/8, 3/4).
7. Use the numbers one to nine and make a triangle with four spaces per side instead of three.
8. Use the numbers one to 12 arranged in a square with four spaces per side.
9. Develop informal proofs explaining the reasons for the smallest and largest possible sum for a given set of numbers.
10. Have older or more advanced students look at the problem algebraically, substituting letters for the numbers and trying to discover a formula that will accurately describe the problem. (See *Solutions* for further details.)

Solutions

These are the four possible solutions for the numbers one to six, as well as some of the patterns that exist. The patterns shown here are by no means exhaustive. Part of the joy of this problem is having your students discover things you have never noticed before.

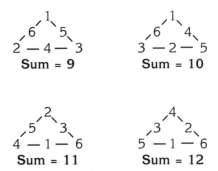

In addition to these four possible sums, there are 20 possible variations derived from the rotations and flips of the above solutions, giving a total of 24 different ways to write the solutions. For example, there are six variations for the sum of nine on a side, as shown.

Sum = 9

Original

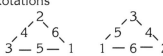

Rotations

```
      1              2              3
   /6   5\        /4   6\        /5   4\
  2 — 4 — 3      3 — 5 — 1      1 — 6 — 2
```

Flips

```
      1              2              3
   /5   6\        /6   4\        /4   5\
  3 — 4 — 2      1 — 5 — 3      2 — 6 — 1
```

Patterns in the Problem

1. The sum of the interior triangle is always a multiple of three.

```
      1                    1
   /6····5\             /6····4\
  2 — 4 — 3            3 — 2 — 5
  6 + 5 + 4 = 15       6 + 4 + 2 = 12

      2                    4
   /5····3\             /3····2\
  4 — 1 — 6            5 — 1 — 6
  5 + 3 + 1 = 9        3 + 2 + 1 = 6
```

2. The sum of the corners is always a multiple of three. (Note that the sums of the corners are exactly opposite of the sums of the interior triangles, i.e. a sum of six in the corners has a sum of 15 in the center, and a sum of 15 in the corners has a sum of six in the center).

```
      1                    1
   /6   5\              /6   4\
  2 — 4 — 3            3 — 2 — 5
  1 + 2 + 3 = 6        1 + 3 + 5 = 9

      2                    4
   /5   3\              /3   2\
  4 — 1 — 6            5 — 1 — 6
  2 + 4 + 6 = 12       4 + 5 + 6 = 15
```

3. The sum of the three small corner triangles within the large triangle is always the same. What is interesting about this is the different numbers that you get for the sum. When the sum of the sides of the triangle is nine, the sum of each corner triangle is 12 (as shown). However, when the sum of the sides of the triangle is 12, the sum of each corner triangle is nine.

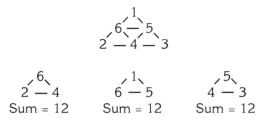

```
   /6\          /1\          /5\
  2 — 4        6 — 5        4 — 3
  Sum = 12     Sum = 12     Sum = 12
```

4. For any six consecutive numbers, placing the smallest numbers in the corners will produce the smallest sum and the placing the largest numbers in the corners will produce the largest sum.

5. If the smallest number in the sequence is odd (**1**-6, **3**-8, **5**-10, etc.), placing the odd numbers in the corners will produce the smaller of the two middle sums. If the smallest number in the sequence is even (**2**-7, **4**-9, **6**-11, etc.), placing the odd numbers in the corners will yield the larger of the two middle sums.

Numbers in corners	Sum of 1-6	Sum of 2-7	Sum of 3-8	Sum of 4-9
Small	9	12	15	18
Odd	10	14	16	20
Even	11	13	17	19
Large	12	15	18	21

6. When odd numbers are in the corners, the target sum will always be even, because whenever you add two odds and an even, the result is even. When even numbers are in the corners, the target sum will be always be odd, because whenever you add two evens and an odd, the result is odd. When the small and large numbers are in the corner, the target sum is sometimes odd and sometimes even. This is because there are both odd and even numbers being counted twice. When the smallest number in the sequence is odd, the smallest target sum will be odd, and the largest even. When the smallest number in the sequence is even, the smallest target sum will be even, and the largest odd.

7. When using consecutive whole numbers, the sum of the numbers being used (1 + 2 + 3 + 4 + 5 + 6) is always a multiple of three (21). Only products of three and odd numbers occur.

Set of Numbers	Sum	Multiple of Three
1 - 6	21	3 x 7
2 - 7	27	3 x 9
3 - 8	33	3 x 11
4 - 9	39	3 x 13
5 - 10	45	3 x 15
6 - 11	51	3 x 17

8. Within a given triangle, the absolute value of the difference between a vertex and the number on the opposite side is always the same.

Difference = 3   Difference = 3   Difference = 3

Extension #10

As mentioned before, there is a constant difference between the vertices and the sides opposite them. If this is viewed algebraically, a new way of thinking about the problem emerges. Let the vertices of the triangle be **a**, **b**, and **c**, and the difference between a vertex and the opposite side be **d**. The triangle now looks like this:

$$a - (a + d) = d \quad b - (b + d) = d \quad c - (c + d) = d$$

Using this formula it becomes possible to generate an infinite number of solutions simply by picking numbers at random. For example, if you choose three, eight, and 10 to be the vertices (**a**, **b**, **c**) and choose a difference of four (**d**), the following solution emerges:

Sum = 25

If you are more intentional about the numbers which you choose, selecting numbers that differ by a constant amount, some interesting patterns begin to develop. When the numbers used are not consecutive, but are separated by the same number, there are always four different sums (solutions) possible. For example, for six numbers separated by three beginning with the number two, the following solutions are possible:

Numbers: 2, 5, 8, 11, 14, 17

Sum = 24
d = 9

Sum = 27
d = 3

Sum = 30
d = 3

Sum = 33
d = 9

When **a**, **b**, and **c** are the smallest numbers (2, 5, 8) or the largest numbers (11, 14, 17) **d** is nine. When **a**, **b**, and **c** are the even numbers (2, 8, 14) or the odd numbers (5, 11, 17), **d** is three. Note that three is the number originally used to generate the sequence, and nine is 3 x 3. If you use other differences to generate number sequences, it becomes clear that this is one of several patterns which hold true for this type of sequence.

1. For each set of numbers that differ by a constant amount, that difference will be the smaller of two possible **d**s that can be obtained using those numbers.
Difference: 4
Numbers: 1, 5, 9, 13, 17, 21

Sum = 27
d = 12

Sum = 39
d = 12

Sum = 31
d = 4

Sum = 35
d = 4

Additionally, the larger **d** is always the smaller **d** multiplied by three.

Difference	Small d		Large d
1	1	(x 3)	3
2	2	(x 3)	6
3	3	(x 3)	9
4	4	(x 3)	12
5	5	(x 3)	15

2. When the amount separating the numbers in the sequence is odd, the sum of the numbers in the sequence adds up to an odd multiple of three. When the difference between the numbers in the sequence is even, the sum of the numbers in the sequence adds up to an even multiple of three.

Difference: 3
   1 + 4 + 7 + 10 + 13 + 16 = 51 (3 x 17)
Difference: 4
   1 + 5 + 9 + 13 + 17 + 21 = 66 (3 x 22)
Difference: 5
   1 + 6 + 11 + 16 + 21 + 26 = 81 (3 x 27)
Difference: 6
   1 + 7 + 13 + 19 + 25 + 31 = 96 (3 x 32)

3. Another pattern to notice within the sums is that, when paired, the numbers in each sequence add up to the multiple of three that their combined totals produce.

For example:
Difference of 3 (3 x 17):
   1 + 16 = 17   4 + 13 = 17   7 + 10 = 17
Difference of 4 (3 x 22):
   1 + 21 = 22   5 + 17 = 22   9 + 13 = 22
Difference of 5 (3 x 27):
   1 + 26 = 27   6 + 21 = 27   11 + 16 = 27
Difference of 6 (3 x 32):
   1 + 31 = 32   7 + 25 = 32   13 + 19 = 32

The Fascinating Triangle

Place the number cards one to six in the spaces below so that the sums of the three numbers on each side of the triangle are equal. Record your solutions on the next page.

The Fascinating Triangle

Record your solutions.

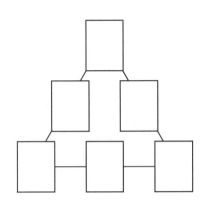

_____
Sum

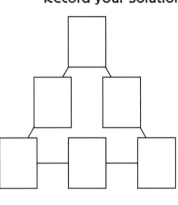

_____
Sum

_____
Sum

_____
Sum

_____
Sum

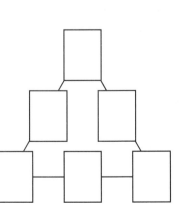

_____
Sum

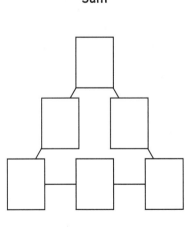

_____
Sum

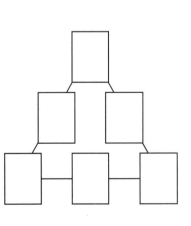

_____
Sum

The Fascinating Triangle

Answer these questions when you have finished searching for solutions.

1. What sums did you find?

2. Do you think you found all of the possible sums for this problem? Why or why not?

3. What patterns do you see in your solutions?

4.   What other discoveries did you make about the Fascinating Triangle?

The Fascinating Triangle

Extensions

What happens when you use the number cards two through seven in the triangle?

How about the numbers three through eight?

List some other possible extensions or questions related to this problem.

Pick one of these extensions and explore it in depth. Be prepared to report your findings.

Cookie Combos

Topic
Visual patterns, divergent thinking

Key Question
How many different ways can you find to count the number of cookies in the arrangement?

Focus
Students will be challenged to use divergent thinking and come up with as many ways of counting 25 cookies as possible.

Guiding Documents
Project 2061 Benchmark
- *Usually there is no one right way to solve a mathematical problem; different methods have different advantages and disadvantages.*

NCTM Standards
- *Explore problems and describe results using graphical, numerical, physical, algebraic and verbal mathematical models or representations*
- *Visualize and represent geometric figures with special attention to developing spatial sense*

Math
Counting

Integrated Processes
Observing

Materials
Student sheets
Butcher paper

Background Information
Unlike many of the activities in this book, the solution to this problem is easily obtained by counting the number of cookies in the arrangement. However, the goal is not to have students find how many cookies there are, but to see how many ways they can count the cookies. This requires divergent thinking and the recognition that there can be many different ways to solve the same problem. This activity is also valuable for another reason—it gives students practice with spatial visualization.

Management
1. To get your class started you may want to make an overhead transparency of the cookie arrangement to use when introducing the activity.
2. This activity is designed to be done using either an open-ended or a structured format. If your class works well without much guidance, hand out the first student sheet and challenge your students to find their own ways of recording the different cookie combinations. If your class needs more direction, distribute both student sheets. The second page gives students a recording scheme that incorporates both numerical and graphical information.
3. During the time of class sharing you may want to create a master list which shows all of the solutions generated by your students. A large sheet of butcher paper or something similar will allow students to record their own findings and share in the discoveries of their classmates.

Procedure
1. Hand out the student sheet(s) and go over the directions. *Find as many different ways to count the number of cookies in the arrangement as possible and record your answers.* If your class needs help getting started, use the overhead transparency to go over a few possible solutions.
2. Give students time to work on the problem, finding as many solutions as they can. Allow them to work in small groups or individually.
3. When everyone has found at least five different ways to count the cookies, come together for a time of class discussion.
4. Have students (groups) record their solutions on the butcher paper. Make sure that all of the different solutions are recorded.

Discussion
1. How many ways did you come up with to count the cookies?
2. What were those ways?
3. What did you learn/discover by doing this problem?

Extensions
1. For older students, have them translate the visual patterns they discover into number sentences. For

example, (4 x 4) + (3 x 3) = 25 is one way of describing the pattern in the diagonal rows of cookies.

2. Challenge students to make a different arrangement of cookies which also allows for various combinations (don't be limited to 25 cookies).

3. Have students come up with number sentences for 25 that can be represented visually in the arrangement.

Solutions

Pictured below are a few of the many solutions your students may discover and their number sentences. Some of the number sentences have been written more than one way. This list is by no means exhaustive, and it is hoped that your students will discover patterns which are not shown here.

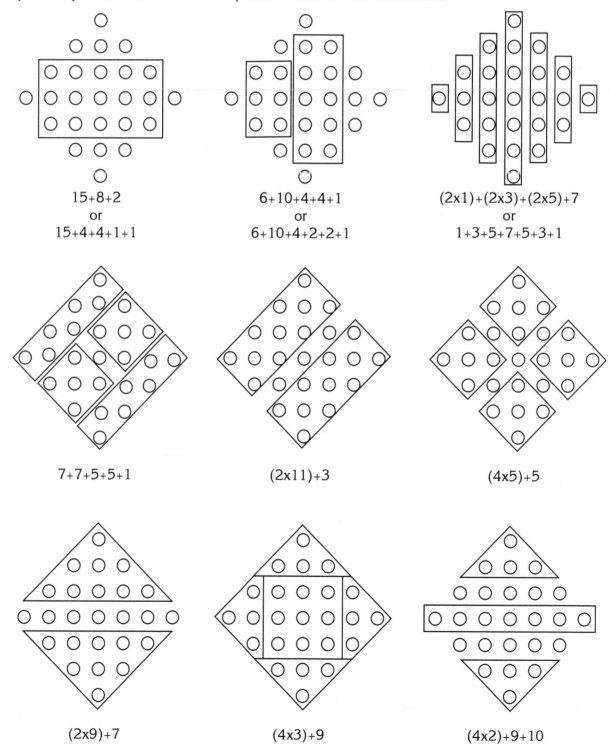

15+8+2
or
15+4+4+1+1

6+10+4+4+1
or
6+10+4+2+2+1

(2x1)+(2x3)+(2x5)+7
or
1+3+5+7+5+3+1

7+7+5+5+1

(2x11)+3

(4x5)+5

(2x9)+7

(4x3)+9

(4x2)+9+10

Cookie Combos

How many cookies are in the arrangement below? Try to find your answer in as many different ways as possible. Make a record of each of these ways.

Cookie Combos

Use this sheet to show how many different ways you found the number of cookies in the arrangement. Try to record your answer in both pictures and numbers.

CALENDAR CAPERS

Topic
Patterns

Key Question
How many patterns can you find on a page from a calendar?

Focus
Students will be challenged to find as many patterns as they can on a page from a calendar and then to try and find mathematical explanations for the patterns.

Guiding Documents
Project 2061 Benchmark
- *Mathematics is the study of many kinds of patterns, including numbers and shapes and operations on them. Sometimes patterns are studied because they help to explain how the world works or how to solve practical problems, sometimes because they are interesting in themselves.*

NCTM Standards
- *Recognize, describe, extend, and create a variety of patterns*
- *Use patterns and relationships to analyze mathematical situations*

Math
Math patterns

Integrated Processes
Observing
Comparing and contrasting
Inferring
Relating
Generalizing
Applying

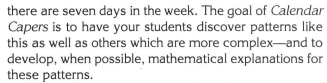

Materials
Student sheets
Markers or colored pencils, optional

Background Information
A wonderful principle of mathematics is that whenever numbers of any kind are arranged according to some rule, patterns emerge. These patterns range from very simple to complex, but they are always present. Since our calendars are based on weeks with seven days, many interesting patterns emerge that revolve around the number seven. For example, a simple pattern is seen by comparing different dates that fall on the same day of the week. They will all be separated by seven, since

there are seven days in the week. The goal of *Calendar Capers* is to have your students discover patterns like this as well as others which are more complex—and to develop, when possible, mathematical explanations for these patterns.

The arithmetic encountered in this activity can range from quite simple to fairly complex. Students can do the activity using only addition and subtraction, or can be pushed to use multiplication, division, averages, fractions, and integers.

Management
1. This activity is designed to be open-ended. It works best if students are in small groups and have the opportunity to interact. Once one person makes a discovery it can be shared with the group immediately, stimulating further discoveries.
2. Two calendar options have been provided for you in this activity. There is a pre-made calendar with dates already set, as well as a template which allows you to enter the dates from whatever month and year you choose. Both of the calendar pages have a corresponding sheet on which students can record the patterns which they discover.
3. It is recommended that students use markers or colored pencils to highlight the patterns they discover. This will help stimulate discoveries by making some of the patterns easier to see.
4. You may want to make an overhead transparency of the calendar page you choose to use. It can be used during the discussion session to allow students to share the patterns they have discovered with the rest of the class.

Procedure
1. Distribute the student sheets and go over the instructions. *Find as many patterns as you can in one calendar month. Don't be limited by linear patterns.*
2. Have students work in small groups and encourage group members to work together to come up with as many solutions as possible.
3. If students are stuck, it may be necessary to guide them through the discovery of one of the easier patterns so that they can see the process.
4. Once students have found a number of patterns, challenge them to discover the mathematical reasons for several of these patterns.
5. After they have had sufficient time to explore, have the groups share the patterns they discovered with the rest of the class and discuss the processes they used to make their discoveries.

Discussion

1. What patterns did you discover in this problem? (See *Solutions*.)
2. What process did you use to discover the patterns?
3. What similarities can you discover in the patterns?
4. Mathematically speaking, what are the reasons for these patterns? (See *Solutions*.)

Solutions

Following are a few of the many patterns your students may discover.

1. The patterns emerging from movement from one space on a calendar to another directly adjoining it in any direction can be represented by the diagram below.

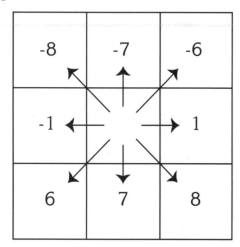

- If you go in a diagonal up and to the left, the numbers are all separated by -8. This is because you are subtracting a week (seven days) and one day.
- If you go straight up, the numbers are separated by -7. This is because you are subtracting one week (seven days).
- If you go in a diagonal up and to the right, the numbers are all separated by -6. This is because you are subtracting one day less than a week (six days).
- If you go one space to the left or right, the numbers are separated by -1 and 1 respectively, because you are either adding or subtracting one day.
- If you go in a diagonal down and to the left, the numbers are all separated by six. This is because you are adding one day less than a week (six days).
- If you go straight down, the numbers are separated by seven. This is because you are adding one week (seven days).
- If you go in a diagonal down and to the right, the numbers are all separated by eight. This is because you are adding a week (seven days) and one day.

2. Any time you move from space to space in the calendar using a constant operation (i.e. go over two and down three) on any number, the difference between the number in the space you start on and the space you end up on will always be the same.

The difference itself will (logically) always be the number of days you are adding to the original number. For example, if you start on the 8th, and go one to the left, and two down, you will be on the 21st. The difference between eight and 21 is 13. If you start on the 3rd and go one to the left and two down, you will be on the 16th. The difference between three and 16 is also 13.

3. If you add the columns, the sums are separated by four if there are four numbers in the column, and by five if there are five numbers in the column. This is because you are adding one to any given number in each row every time you move a column to the right. When there are four rows, you are adding a total of four to the column, but when there are five rows, you are adding a total of five.

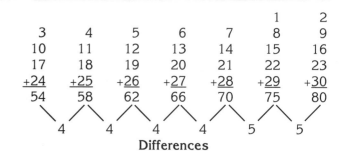

Differences

4. When looking at blocks of numbers, the sums of the diagonals are the same. For example, a 2 x 2 square might contain the numbers:

1	2
8	9

or

6	7
13	14

The sum of $1 + 9 = 10$ and the sum of $2 + 8 = 10$. Likewise, $6 + 14 = 20$ and $7 + 13 = 20$. It follows then that the sum of all the numbers in the block can be obtained by doubling the diagonal. $1 + 2 + 8 + 9 = 20$, $10 \times 2 = 20$ and $6 + 7 + 13 + 14 = 40$, $2 \times 20 = 40$.

This same principle also works for 3x3 squares. For example:

11	12	13
18	19	20
25	26	27

$11 + 19 + 27 = 57$
$25 + 19 + 13 = 57$

In 3 x 3 squares, the sum is also found in the middle row and column, but not in the outer rows and columns.

$12 + 19 + 26 = 57$ $11 + 12 + 13 = 36$ $11 + 18 + 25 = 54$
$18 + 19 + 20 = 57$ $25 + 26 + 27 = 78$ $13 + 20 + 27 = 60$

However, the average of the outer rows and columns equals the sum of the diagonal. 78 + 36 = 114, 114 ÷ 2 = 57; 54 + 60 = 114, 114 ÷ 2 = 57; 78 + 36 + 54 + 60 = 228, 228 ÷ 4 = 57.

Unlike a 2 x 2 square, doubling the diagonal does not give the sum of the square. Instead, tripling the diagonal gives the sum of the numbers in the 3 x 3 square.

$$11 + 12 + 13 + 18 + 19 + 20 + 25 + 26 + 27 = 171$$
$$3 \times 57 = 171$$

The sum of all the numbers in the square can also be found by multiplying the middle number by nine.

$$11 + 12 + 13 + 18 + 19 + 20 + 25 + 26 + 27 = 171$$
$$9 \times 19 = 171.$$

This works because in a 3 x 3 square, the middle number is the average of the three numbers in of each of the rows, columns and diagonals that pass through the center.

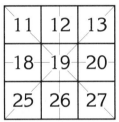

$$11 + 19 + 27 = 57$$
$$12 + 19 + 29 = 57$$
$$13 + 19 + 25 = 57$$
$$18 + 19 + 20 = 57$$
$$57 \div 3 = 19$$

It also works because the middle number in a 3 x 3 square is the average of all nine numbers.

$$11 + 12 + 13 + 18 + 19 + 20 + 25 + 26 + 27 = 171$$
$$171 \div 9 = 19$$

5. In a month with 30 days, those days can be divided in three ways without a remainder: 5 x 6, 3 x 10, and 2 x 15. If you look at groupings of numbers based on these divisions, some interesting patterns emerge.

Numbers	Sum	Difference
1 - 5	15	
6 - 10	40	40 - 15 = 25
11 - 15	65	65 - 40 = 25
16 - 20	90	90 - 65 = 25
21 - 25	115	115 - 90 = 25
26 - 30	140	140 - 115 = 25
1 - 6	21	
7 - 12	57	57 - 21 = 36
13 - 18	93	93 - 57 = 36
19 - 24	129	129 - 93 = 36
25 - 30	165	165 - 129 = 36

This pattern continues, with each of the groupings listed above. The difference between the sums always equals the number of dates in the set squared. When you add every three numbers, the difference between the sums is nine. When you add every 10 numbers, the difference between the sums is 100, and so on.

6. If you look at blocks of numbers that are rectangular in shape, some interesting patterns occur. In a 2 x 3 rectangle, the sum of all the numbers in the rectangle is the sum of the middle column multiplied by three. For example:

8	9	10
15	16	17

$$8 + 9 + 10 + 15 + 16 + 17 = 75$$
$$9 + 16 = 25$$
$$3 \times 25 = 75$$

The same pattern holds true in 2 x 5 rectangles. For example:

13	14	15	16	17
20	21	22	23	24

$$13 + 14 + 15 + 16 + 17 + 20 + 21 + 22 + 23 + 24 = 185$$
$$15 + 22 = 37$$
$$5 \times 37 = 185$$

Notice that instead of multiplying the sum of the middle column by three, we multiplied it by five because there are five columns, not three.

In fact, whenever you have an arithmetic sequence (e.g., 2, 3, 4, 5, 6; or 1, 3, 5, 7; or 10, 20, 30, 40, etc.) with an odd number of elements, the average of the numbers in that sequence is always the middle number.

In 2 x 4 rectangle where there is no middle column, things become a bit more complicated. To find the sum of all the numbers in this situation, there are three options. The first is to take the sum of the middle two rows and double it. For example:

2	3	4	5
9	10	11	12

$$2 + 3 + 4 + 5 + 9 + 10 + 11 + 12 = 56$$
$$3 + 4 + 10 + 11 = 28$$
$$2 \times 28 = 56$$

The second option is to take the sum of either of the two middle diagonals and multiply it by four.

6	7	8	9
12	13	14	15

6 + 7 + 8 + 9 + 12 + 13 +14 + 15 = 84
7 + 14 = 21
8 + 13 = 21
4 x 21 = 84

The third option is to create a middle column using fractions, find the sum of that, and multiply it by four. For example:

15	16	17	18
22	23	24	25

15 + 16 + 17 + 18 + 22 + 23 +24 + 25 = 160
16.5 + 23.5 = 40
4 x 40 = 160

CALENDAR CAPERS

January 2001

Sunday	Monday	Tuesday	Wednesday	Thursday	Friday	Saturday
	1	2	3	4	5	6
7	8	9	10	11	12	13
14	15	16	17	18	19	20
21	22	23	24	25	26	27
28	29	30	31			

CALENDAR CAPERS

January 2001

Sunday	Monday	Tuesday	Wednesday	Thursday	Friday	Saturday
	1	2	3	4	5	6
7	8	9	10	11	12	13
14	15	16	17	18	19	20
21	22	23	24	25	26	27
28	29	30	31			

January 2001

Sunday	Monday	Tuesday	Wednesday	Thursday	Friday	Saturday
	1	2	3	4	5	6
7	8	9	10	11	12	13
14	15	16	17	18	19	20
21	22	23	24	25	26	27
28	29	30	31			

January 2001

Sunday	Monday	Tuesday	Wednesday	Thursday	Friday	Saturday
	1	2	3	4	5	6
7	8	9	10	11	12	13
14	15	16	17	18	19	20
21	22	23	24	25	26	27
28	29	30	31			

January 2001

Sunday	Monday	Tuesday	Wednesday	Thursday	Friday	Saturday
	1	2	3	4	5	6
7	8	9	10	11	12	13
14	15	16	17	18	19	20
21	22	23	24	25	26	27
28	29	30	31			

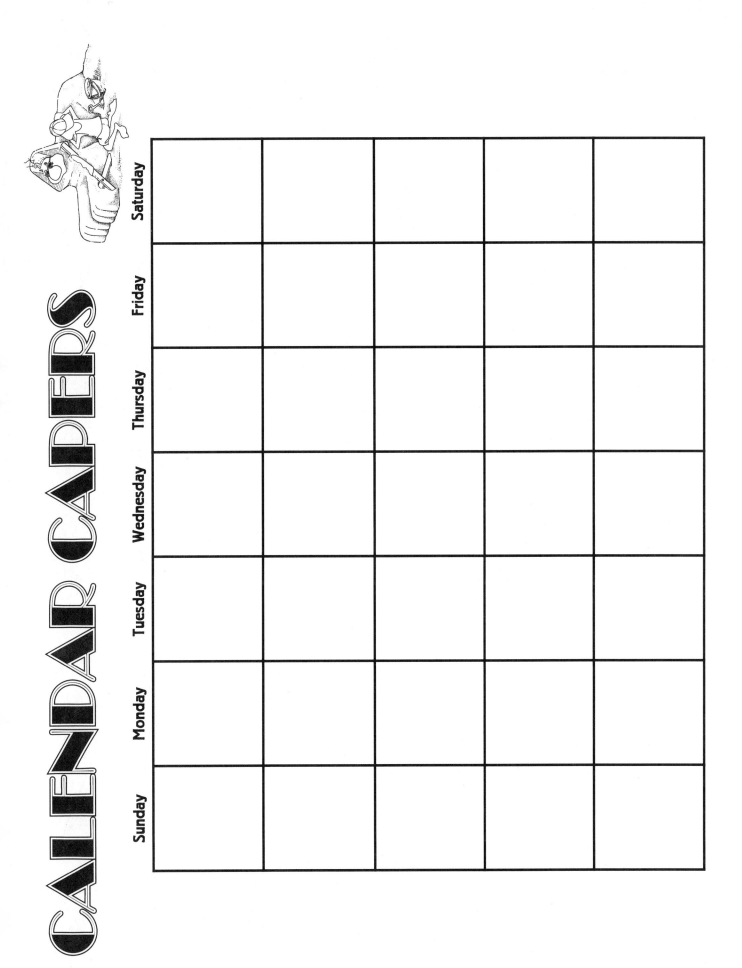

CALENDAR CAPERS

Sunday	Monday	Tuesday	Wednesday	Thursday	Friday	Saturday

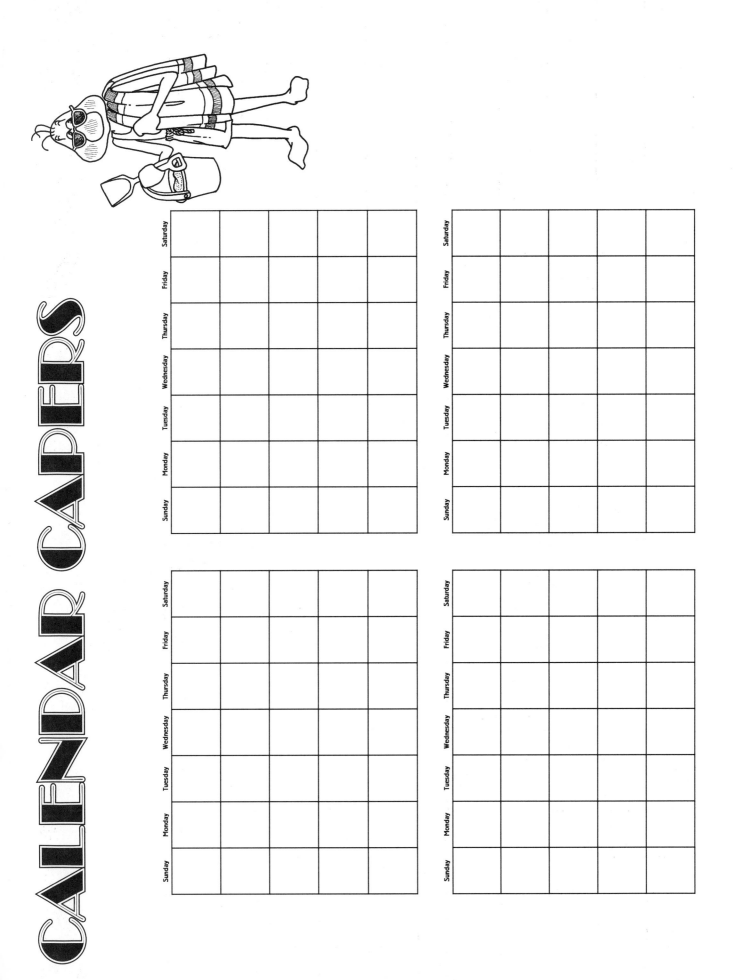

CALENDAR CAPERS

Sunday	Monday	Tuesday	Wednesday	Thursday	Friday	Saturday

Sunday	Monday	Tuesday	Wednesday	Thursday	Friday	Saturday

Sunday	Monday	Tuesday	Wednesday	Thursday	Friday	Saturday

Sunday	Monday	Tuesday	Wednesday	Thursday	Friday	Saturday

CALENDAR CAPERS

There are many amazing patterns in calendars that are fun to explore. How many patterns can you discover in one calendar month? Don't be limited by linear patterns. How about blocks of numbers? List and share your discoveries.

I've Got Your Number

Topic
Developing a mathematical strategy

Key Question
How can you discover which number from one to 100 your partner has chosen in the fewest guesses?

Focus
Students will learn to develop and justify a mathematical strategy for guessing an unknown number from one to 100 in the fewest possible tries.

Guiding Document
NCTM Standards
- *Recognize and apply deductive and inductive reasoning*
- *Justify their answers and solution processes*

Math
Numbers
Math strategy

Integrated Processes
Observing
Generalizing
Interpreting data

Materials
Student sheet
Overhead projector
Overhead transparency and pens

Background Information
This activity is an open-ended strategy game similar to 20 questions in which a student tries to guess his/her partner's number in as few tries as possible by asking yes/no questions. As students play this game, they should soon develop strategies for determining the number in the fewest tries each time. This activity exercises students' logical thinking skills and challenges them to justify their strategies by showing that they work with any number.

Management
1. This activity is designed as a game to be played first as a class, then in pairs. Make an overhead transparency of the hundreds chart provided to use in the whole-class section.

2. When playing as a class, use the overhead projector and transparency to mark off the appropriate spaces as students make their guesses. Make a tally mark in the box at the bottom of the transparency for each guess. At first, students will probably ask questions that eliminate only one number at a time. Because of this, it is a good idea to limit them to 20 questions. After a few rounds, someone will likely ask a question which eliminates more than one number (e.g., Is the number between one and ten?). Once this happens, students will realize that the type of questions asked makes a difference and will be ready to play the game with each other.

3. When introducing the game and playing it as a class, be careful not to give your students any strategy hints. While good questions seem obvious to adults (and perhaps to older children), it is important for students to discover the principle of eliminating many numbers with a single question on their own.

4. You may find it necessary to make enough copies of the student sheet for each student to have two copies. This will allow students the opportunity to play the game more than four times to develop their strategies.

5. While this game primarily focuses on developing a mathematical strategy, it also provides the opportunity for students to develop their mathematical vocabulary. To play this game at the most basic level, students must be able to grasp concepts such as greater than/less than and odd/even. However, the opportunity is there for students to have a sophisticated dialogue using mathematical terms to eliminate numbers (see *Solutions* for examples).

Procedure
1. Introduce the game and explain the rules to the class. *I am thinking of a number between one and 100. Try to find that number by asking questions that can only be answered by yes or no. I will keep track of how many guesses it takes. Try to find the number in the fewest number of guesses.*

2. Using the overhead, play the game as a class until the students begin to discover that the types of questions they ask make a difference.

3. Have each student choose a partner (or assign pairs) and hand out the student sheet to each person. Explain that this sheet is to be used when they are guessing their partner's number.

4. To prevent a student from forgetting or changing his/her number mid-game, suggest that it be written down somewhere at the start of each game. When the partner guesses correctly, the number can be verified by showing it.

5. Have students play the game until their strategies have developed to a point where they can consistently find their partners' number in under ten guesses. A minimum of six or seven guesses is necessary if students don't make a lucky guess. Give students extra sheets as necessary.

6. Regroup for a time of class discussion where students share their various strategies and justify their ability to consistently find any number in no more than six or seven guesses.

Discussion

1. What strategy did you develop for finding your partner's number?

2. What made you decide to use this strategy? [Various. It got rid of lots of numbers at once, etc.]

3. Using your strategy, what is the fewest number of questions you can ask to find your partner's number, if you don't get a lucky guess? [six or seven, hopefully]

4. Why is this? (See *Solutions*.)

5. What other kinds of questions could you ask that would also let you find the number in six or seven guesses? (See *Solutions*.)

Extensions

1. Limit the kinds of questions students can ask. For example, no greater than/less than questions. (See *Solutions* for suggestions.)

2. Increase the range of numbers to 1–500 or 1–1000 and determine the minimum number of guesses necessary to consistently find the number.

3. Determine the maximum range of numbers that can be handled using any number of guesses. (Hint: This is related to powers of two.)

Solutions

When dealing with 100 numbers, it is possible to find the number in six or seven guesses every time. This is possible by asking questions that divide the remaining numbers in half each time. Therefore, beginning with 100 numbers:

Guess 1: 50 numbers left
Guess 2: 25 numbers left
Guess 3: 12 or 13 numbers left
Guess 4: 6 or 7 numbers left
Guess 5: 3 or 4 numbers left
Guess 6: 1 or 2 numbers left
(Guess 7: 1 number left)

The easiest way to reduce the numbers by half is to ask a greater than/less than question such as: *Is the number greater than 49?* However, there are several other questions which eliminate many numbers at once, and are slightly more mathematical in nature. For example,

1. Is the number odd/even?
2. Is the digit in the ten's place odd/even?
3. Is the number a multiple of 3, 4, 5, etc.?
4. Is the number a factor of 20, 24, 32, etc.?
5. Is the number prime?

Therefore, a strategy which uses questions of a more mathematical nature might go something like this:

Q: Is the number odd?
A: Yes.
Q: Is it greater than 50?
A: No.
Q: Is the digit in the ten's place odd?
A: Yes.
Q: Is the digit in the ten's place a one?
A: No.
Q: Is the number prime?
A: No.
Q: Is the number 39?
A: No.
Q: Then it must be 35!
A: That's right!

I've Got Your Number

Your teacher is thinking of a number on the chart below. Try to find that number by asking questions that can only be answered by yes or no. Your teacher will keep track of how many guesses it takes. Try to find the number in the fewest number of guesses.

1	2	3	4	5	6	7	8	9	10
11	12	13	14	15	16	17	18	19	20
21	22	23	24	25	26	27	28	29	30
31	32	33	34	35	36	37	38	39	40
41	42	43	44	45	46	47	48	49	50
51	52	53	54	55	56	57	58	59	60
61	62	63	64	65	66	67	68	69	70
71	72	73	74	75	76	77	78	79	80
81	82	83	84	85	86	87	88	89	90
91	92	93	94	95	96	97	98	99	100

Number of Guesses:

I've Got Your Number

This game is made to be played with a partner. Your partner will write a number between one and 100 on a separate sheet of paper without showing it to you. Try to guess your partner's number by asking questions that can only be answered yes or no. Use this sheet to record your guesses. In the grids below, mark off the number(s) that each guess eliminates, and in the boxes keep track of the number of guesses you make by drawing a tally for each one. Once you have guessed your partner's number, switch roles and have your partner try to guess your number.

Game 1

1	2	3	4	5	6	7	8	9	10
11	12	13	14	15	16	17	18	19	20
21	22	23	24	25	26	27	28	29	30
31	32	33	34	35	36	37	38	39	40
41	42	43	44	45	46	47	48	49	50
51	52	53	54	55	56	57	58	59	60
61	62	63	64	65	66	67	68	69	70
71	72	73	74	75	76	77	78	79	80
81	82	83	84	85	86	87	88	89	90
91	92	93	94	95	96	97	98	99	100

Game 2

1	2	3	4	5	6	7	8	9	10
11	12	13	14	15	16	17	18	19	20
21	22	23	24	25	26	27	28	29	30
31	32	33	34	35	36	37	38	39	40
41	42	43	44	45	46	47	48	49	50
51	52	53	54	55	56	57	58	59	60
61	62	63	64	65	66	67	68	69	70
71	72	73	74	75	76	77	78	79	80
81	82	83	84	85	86	87	88	89	90
91	92	93	94	95	96	97	98	99	100

1	2	3	4	5	6	7	8	9	10
11	12	13	14	15	16	17	18	19	20
21	22	23	24	25	26	27	28	29	30
31	32	33	34	35	36	37	38	39	40
41	42	43	44	45	46	47	48	49	50
51	52	53	54	55	56	57	58	59	60
61	62	63	64	65	66	67	68	69	70
71	72	73	74	75	76	77	78	79	80
81	82	83	84	85	86	87	88	89	90
91	92	93	94	95	96	97	98	99	100

Game 3

1	2	3	4	5	6	7	8	9	10
11	12	13	14	15	16	17	18	19	20
21	22	23	24	25	26	27	28	29	30
31	32	33	34	35	36	37	38	39	40
41	42	43	44	45	46	47	48	49	50
51	52	53	54	55	56	57	58	59	60
61	62	63	64	65	66	67	68	69	70
71	72	73	74	75	76	77	78	79	80
81	82	83	84	85	86	87	88	89	90
91	92	93	94	95	96	97	98	99	100

Game 4

After you have played this game several times, try to develop a strategy to help you find your partner's number in the fewest number of guesses. Use the back of this sheet to describe your strategy.

Challenge: What is the minimum number of guesses you need to consistently find your partner's number? Justify your answer.

Deals on Wheels

Topic
Multiple solutions

Key Question
What are all the possible combinations of bicycles, tricycles, and wagons if there are 17 wheels total?

Focus
Students will solve a problem with multiple solutions.

Guiding Document
NCTM Standards
- *Formulate problems from everyday and mathematical situations*
- *Justify their answers and solution processes*

Math
Multiple solutions
Whole number operations

Integrated Processes
Observing
Classifying

Materials
Student sheets

Background Information
Many students believe that the main task in mathematics is to find *the* answer (emphasis on the singular). This may happen because they have not encountered many problems with more than one solution. This activity provides a way to challenge that notion by offering a problem with multiple solutions.

The ability to solve one problem in several different ways is an important mathematical skill that will serve students in other subject areas as well. This activity provides the opportunity for students to develop and improve that skill.

Management
1. This activity is designed to be done using either an open-ended or a structured format. The first student sheet is for an open-ended format, the second sheet is for a more structured format. Choose which method is best for your class and hand out the appropriate sheet.
2. For those students who need the aid of manipulatives, the pictures on the third student sheet can be cut out and used to help solve the problem.

Procedure
1. Hand out student sheet one or two and manipulatives, if needed. Go over the instructions. *What are all the possible combinations of bicycles, tricycles, and wagons that can be in Beverly's workroom if there are 17 wheels total?*
2. Have students work in small groups or by themselves to come up with all of the possible combinations.
3. Close with a time of class discussion to go over the solutions and the reasoning behind them.

Discussion
1. How many possible combinations are there? [eight]
2. How do you know that you got them all?
3. Did you discover anything interesting about the combinations that were possible? Explain. [Various. There always has to be a tricycle, etc.]
4. Why can't you have a combination without a tricycle? [Seventeen is an odd number, without a tricycle, you would only get even numbers of wheels.]
5. Why isn't there ever an even number of tricycles? [Because having an even number of tricycles gives you an even number, and there is an odd number of wheels.]

Extensions
1. Add unicycles to the list of possibilities. (Be prepared to spend some time with this extension as there are well over 20 solutions!)
2. Have students solve for numbers other than 17 and compare the solutions.
3. Challenge older students to do an informal proof for why a tricycle is needed in any combination.

Solutions

Bicycles (2 Wheels)	Tricycles (3 Wheels)	Wagons (4 Wheels)
1	1	3
3	1	2
5	1	1
7	1	0
0	3	2
2	3	1
4	3	0
1	5	0

Deals on Wheels

Beverly's Bike Bonanza sells bicycles, tricycles, and wagons. Beverly became a math teacher before embarking in the bicycling business. Since she values mathematical thinking, she offers discounts to customers who demonstrate dexterity in mathematical deliberations. Upon entering her store, Beverly tells you that she has 17 wheels in her back workroom, all attached to an unknown (to you) combination of bicycles, tricycles, and wagons. If you can tell her all the possible combinations of the above vehicles that might be in the workroom (no peeking allowed!), you will be entitled to a 10% discount on any purchase. What combinations of bicycles, tricycles, and wagons might the workroom contain?

SERVICE DEPT.
Ask How You Can
Get A 10% Discount

17 ?
Wheels?
?

© 1999 AIMS Education Foundation

Deals on Wheels

The local bike store sells bicycles, tricycles, and wagons. There are 17 wheels in the store and each wheel is attached to one or more of the above vehicles. What combinations of bicycles, tricycles, and wagons might the inventory of the store include? Use the chart to help you find all the possible solutions.

Solution	Number of Bicycles	Number of Bicycle Wheels	Number of Tricycles	Number of Tricycle Wheels	Number of Wagons	Number of Wagon Wheels
1						
2						
3						
4						
5						
6						
7						
8						

Two Digit Turn-Around

Topic
Numbers and number operations

Key Question
What happens when two-digit numbers are subtracted according to a certain procedure?

Focus
Students will practice basic arithmetic facts by subtracting two-digit numbers. They will then look for the many patterns in this process.

Guiding Documents
Project 2061 Benchmark
- *Mathematics is the study of many kinds of patterns, including number and shapes and operations on them. Sometimes patterns are studied because they help to explain how the world works or how to solve practical problems, sometimes because they are interesting in themselves.*

NCTM Standard
- *Recognize, describe, extend, and create variety of patterns*

Math
Whole number operations
Math patterns
Integer operations, optional

Integrated Processes
Observing
Comparing and contrasting
Interpreting data

Materials
Student sheet

Background Information
Two-Digit Turn Around examines some of the fascinating patterns that occur when numbers and number operations are studied in depth. This activity provides students with valuable practice in basic arithmetic skills, while simultaneously placing them in a unique problem-solving environment. It has the added benefit of being adjustable to suit many skill levels. While the main part of the activity examines the problem arithmetically, there are extensions which ask students to work with integers and deal with the problem algebraically.

Management
1. This activity can be done in both an open-ended and a structured format, depending on the needs of your students. Student sheet one presents the problem and allows students to organize their answers however they choose. Student sheet two provides students with a table in which to write their answers. Choose the student sheet which is most appropriate for your class.
2. Some of the patterns in this problem are quite obvious, others are more difficult to find. You may need to encourage students to search for the more difficult patterns.

Procedure
1. Hand out the student sheet that is appropriate for your class and make sure everyone understands the procedure. *Start with a two-digit number where the first digit, the digit in the tens place, is greater than the second. Reverse these two digits and subtract the resulting number from the original number.*
2. Give students sufficient time to do the computation on their own.
3. Allow them to work in groups or by themselves to look for patterns in the answers.
4. Have a time of class discussion where students share their discoveries with each other. If necessary, help the class discover some of the less obvious patterns (see *Solutions*).

Discussion
1. What patterns did you notice in the answers to the subtraction problems? [Various. All answers are a multiple of nine, etc.]
2. Why do you think these patterns occur?

Extensions
1. If students can work with integers, have them find the answers for all possible combinations, even those which produce negative solutions (e.g., 78 - 87, 58 - 85, etc.). An extra column has been added to the chart on the second student sheet to accommodate for this.
2. Challenge older students to use algebraic methods to show why certain patterns occur (see *Solutions*).
3. Explore what happens when this process is applied to three or four numbers instead of two.

Solutions

The table from the structured student sheet is shown below with the correct values inserted. The integer solutions have been included as well.

90 -09 81	91 -19 72	92 -29 63	93 -39 54	94 -49 45	95 -59 36	96 -69 27	97 -79 18	98 -89 9	99 -99 0
80 -08 72	81 -18 63	82 -28 54	83 -38 45	84 -48 36	85 -58 27	86 -68 18	87 -78 9	88 -88 0	89 -98 -9
70 -07 63	71 -17 54	72 -27 45	73 -37 36	74 -47 27	75 -57 18	76 -67 9	77 -77 0	78 -87 -9	79 -97 -18
60 -06 54	61 -16 45	62 -26 36	63 -36 27	64 -46 18	65 -56 9	66 -66 0	67 -76 -9	68 -86 -18	69 -96 -27
50 -05 45	51 -15 36	52 -25 27	53 -35 18	54 -45 9	55 -55 0	56 -65 -9	57 -75 -18	58 -85 -27	59 -95 -36
40 -04 36	41 -14 27	42 -24 18	43 -34 9	44 -44 0	45 -54 -9	46 -64 -18	47 -74 -27	48 -84 -36	49 -94 -45
30 -03 27	31 -13 18	32 -23 9	33 -33 0	34 -43 -9	35 -53 -18	36 -63 -27	37 -73 -36	38 -83 -45	39 -93 -54
20 -02 18	21 -12 9	22 -22 0	23 -32 -9	24 -42 -18	25 -52 -27	26 -62 -36	27 -72 -45	28 -82 -54	29 -92 -63
10 -01 9	11 -11 0	12 -21 -9	13 -31 -18	14 -41 -27	15 -51 -36	16 -61 -45	17 -71 -54	18 -81 -63	19 -91 -72

Patterns

Following is a discussion of some of the patterns which your students may discover in this problem. This list is not exhaustive, and there may be things your students discover which are not listed below.

1. The differences are all multiples of nine (81, 72, 63, 54, 45, 36, 27, 18, 9).

2. There are nine two-digit numbers in the 90s in which the first digit is larger than the second (90 - 98), eight in the 80s (80 - 87), seven in the 70s (70 - 76), etc.

3. The answer to the problem can be obtained by taking the difference between the digits in the larger number and multiplying it by nine.

71	7 - 1 = 6	95	9 - 5 = 4
-17	6 x 9 = **54**	-59	4 x 9 = **36**
54		**36**	

4. The above can be shown algebraically as follows: If ab is a two-digit number with a > b, then (10a + b) - (10b + a) = 9a - 9b = 9(a - b).

   For example:

   83 is a two-digit number with 8 > 3, then [10(8) +3] - [10(3) + 8] = 9(8) - 9(3) = 9(8-3) = 9(5) = 45

5. When expanding the problem to include negative solutions (as in *Extension 1*), the answers follow the same pattern. The negative solutions are the multiples of nine, with the difference between the digits in the smaller number multiplied by nine giving you the solution.

78	7 - 8 = -1
-87	9 x -1 = **-9**
-9	

68	6 - 8 = -2
-86	9 x -2 = **-18**
-18	

58	5 - 8 = -3
-85	9 x -3 = **-27**
-27	

6. There is an interesting pattern when the sum of the digits in either number of a given problem is compared to the digit in the one's place of the answer. When the digit in the one's place is subtracted from the sum of the digits there is a difference of eight for numbers in the 90s, a difference of six for numbers in the 80s, four in the 70s, and so on. As you can see by looking at the examples below, the difference continues to decrease by two until it reaches a difference of -8 for numbers in the tens.

91	9 + 1 = 10	92	9 + 2 = 11
-19	10 - 2 = **8**	-29	11 - 3 = **8**
72		63	

93	9 + 3 = 12	... 98	9 + 8 = 17
-39	12 - 4 = **8**	-89	17 - 9 = **8**
54		9	

81	8 + 1 = 9
-18	9 - 3 = **6**
63	

71	7 + 1 = 8
-17	8 - 4 = **4**
54	

61	6 + 1 = 7
-16	7 - 5 = **2**
45	

51	5 + 1 = 6
-15	6 - 6 = **0**
36	

41	4 + 1 = 5
-14	5 - 7 = **-2**
27	

31	3 + 1 = 4
-13	4 - 8 = **-4**
18	

21	2 + 1 = 3
-12	3 - 9 = **-6**
9	

10	1 + 0 = 1
-01	1 - 9 = **-8**
9	

Two Digit Turn-Around

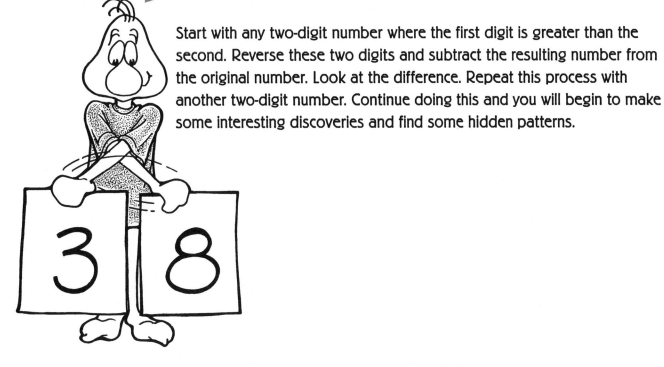

Start with any two-digit number where the first digit is greater than the second. Reverse these two digits and subtract the resulting number from the original number. Look at the difference. Repeat this process with another two-digit number. Continue doing this and you will begin to make some interesting discoveries and find some hidden patterns.

Organize your findings and report them to the rest of the class.

Two Digit Turn-Around

Something very interesting happens when you take a two-digit number with the tens digit greater than the ones, and then reverse these digits and subtract the resulting number from the original number. There are some exciting discoveries and hidden patterns just waiting to be found. Fill in the chart below to help you in your search.

90 - 09	91 - 19	92 - 29	93 - 39	94 - 49	95 - 59	96 - 69	97 - 79	98 - 89	99 - 99
80 - 08	81 - 18	82 - 28							
70 - 07									
20 - 02									
10 - 01									

Organize your findings and share them with the rest of the class.

Topic
Mathematical reasoning

Key Question
How can you figure out the number of children and horses in a corral from information about the number of heads, tails, and feet present?

Focus
Students will be required to use mathematical reasoning to discover the answer to several word problems.

Guiding Documents
Project 2061 Benchmark
- *Usually there is no one right way to solve a mathematical problem; different methods have different advantages and disadvantages.*

NCTM Standards
- *Develop and apply strategies to solve a wide variety of problems*
- *Justify their answers and solution processes*

Math
Mathematical reasoning
Algebraic thinking
Counting

Integrated Processes
Observing
Inferring
Applying

Materials
Student sheet
Chart paper
Markers
Manipulatives, optional

Background Information
This activity has two problems of varying difficulty. The first is an easy one-step story problem, but the second has several steps, and requires thinking that is a little more algebraic in nature. With the help of manipulatives, trial-and-error, and mathematical reasoning, most students should be able to solve this problem.

Management
1. Depending on the age and ability of your students, you may want to provide manipulatives of some kind to make this problem easier for them to handle. Another possibility is to use smaller numbers in the problem to make it suitable for younger children.
2. Each group will need chart paper or something similar on which to record their solutions and the methods they used to arrive at those solutions. This step can end up being the most valuable part of this activity. Not only does it give you insight into your students' thought processes, it forces them to organize their thoughts in a coherent and presentable manner.

Procedure
1. Hand out the student sheet (and manipulatives, if desired) and make sure everyone understands the problems.
2. Have students work in groups to answer both questions.
3. Give students chart paper and markers with which to record their solutions for both problems and the methods they used to arrive at those solutions. The students can also write additional problems on the chart paper.
4. Close with a time of class discussion where the groups share their papers with the rest of the class and compare solutions and methods.

Discussion
1. How many children are there in the first question? [34] ... horses? [29]
2. How did you get that answer? [Various. I subtracted the number of tails from the number of heads, etc.]
3. How many children are there in the second question? [9] How many horses? [13]

4. How did you get that answer?
5. Which question was more difficult? [the second] Why? [Various. It required more than one step, etc.]
6. What additional problems did you try?

Extensions
1. Have each group make up several word problems of their own, and trade these with other groups to find the solutions.
2. Challenge more advanced students to work out an algebraic formula that will allow them to solve for n heads and n tails.

Solutions
1. The solution to the first problem is a straightforward one. To find the number of children and the number of horses, simply subtract the number of tails from the number of heads. Since children do not have tails, that number indicates how many horses are present, and the remainder is the number of children.

$$\begin{array}{rl} 63 & \text{heads} \\ \underline{-29} & \text{tails} \\ 34 & \text{children} \end{array}$$

2. The solution to the second problem is more complex and involves a few more steps. There are numerous ways to solve it, including trial and error. The following method is only one of the many possible ways. The first step is for students to recognize that the number of heads (22) represents the total number of children and horses present.

From there, their task is to discover how many of those 22 are children, and how many are horses. There are twelve combinations of numbers that produce 22:

$$\begin{array}{rr} 22, & 0 \\ 21, & 1 \\ 20, & 2 \\ 19, & 3 \\ 18, & 4 \\ 17, & 5 \\ 16, & 6 \\ 15, & 7 \\ 14, & 8 \\ 13, & 9 \\ 12, & 10 \\ 11, & 11 \end{array}$$

Taking these numbers and multiplying one by four (the number of feet on a pony) and one by two (the number of feet on a child) allows you to discover which combination will give you 70 feet.

Total Number of Heads	Horses	Children	Total Number of Feet
22	20	2	84
22	17	5	78
22	15	7	74
22	13	9	70

The solution is 13 horses and 9 children for a total of 22 heads and 70 feet.

Farmer Fran has a pony ranch which children like to visit. One day a group of children came to visit and entered the corral. Farmer Fran wanted to know how many of her horses and how many children were in the corral so she sent Farmhand Fred to count. He told her that he counted 63 heads and 29 tails in the corral. Help Farmer Fran figure out how many horses and how many children were in the corral.

On a different day, another group of children came to visit. Farmer Fran sent Farmhand Fred to count again. He told her there were 22 heads and 70 feet. How many children and how many horses were in the corral this time?

Extension: Make up your own problems to work on.

Hurkle Hide and Seek

Topic
Problem solving, coordinates

Key Question
How many guesses does it take to find the hurkle on a ten by ten grid?

Focus
Students will try to find the hurkle by guessing co-ordinate points on a ten by ten grid. With each guess they will be given a directional clue to help them find the hurkle.

Guiding Documents
Project 2061 Benchmark
- *It takes two numbers to locate a point on a map or any other flat surface.*

NCTM Standard
- *Develop and apply strategies to solve a wide variety of problems*

Math
Problem solving
Coordinate planes/numbers

Integrated Processes
Observing
Interpreting data
Inferring
Applying

Materials
Student sheet
Overhead transparency and pens

Background Information
Hurkle Hide and Seek is a non-computer version of *Hurkle*, the public-domain computer program. It can be used to introduce the computer game or as a stand-alone game. This activity requires students to find the location of the imaginary and invisible hurkle, which is hiding at one of the coordinate points on a ten by ten grid. With each guess students are given a directional clue to guide their next inquiry. This activity has the advantage of combining logical strategies, problem-solving skills, coordinate numbers, and compass directions, making it a rich problem for your class.

Management
1. You will need to make an overhead transparency of the first sheet to use when playing the game with your class.
2. This game is designed in two parts: a whole-class section, and a partner's section. The purpose of the whole-class section is to get your students familiar with the game so that they can play it on their own with a partner. Because of this, it is important that you do not move on from the first part until everyone understands the game clearly.
3. In order to play this game, all of your students must be able to work with the compass directions and (x, y) coordinates. If they are not, a quick overview will be necessary.
4. When you play as a class, you will "hide" the hurkle by choosing a coordinate point, and then call on individual students to guess the hurkle's location. With each guess, put a number on the overhead (at the point guessed) and give a directional clue from that point to where the hurkle is hiding. For example, if you hide the hurkle at (2, 9) and the first student guesses (7, 3), write 1 (for guess number one) on the point (7, 3) and tell the class that the hurkle is still hiding to the northeast. The *Solutions* section gives an example of how a game might proceed.
5. It is a good idea to laminate the student sheet or copy it onto overhead transparencies and provide students with dry erase or water-soluble markers. This will cut down on waste by allowing them to play as many games as they want on a single sheet of paper. If you are not able to do this, you will probably need to make some extra copies of the student sheet for those who want to play the game more than four times.
6. When students are playing the game in pairs, have the person who is hiding the hurkle write down the coordinate point on a separate sheet of paper so it isn't forgotten and its position accidentally changed mid-game.

Procedure
1. Introduce the game and go over the instructions. *An invisible creature called a hurkle is hiding at one of the intersections of this grid. Your challenge is to find the hurkle in as few guesses as possible. To guess, give a pair of numbers. The first number comes from the x (bottom) axis and the second*

number comes from the y (side) axis. For each guess, you will be given a directional clue to help you find the hurkle.

2. Play the game as a class several times, or until the students are proficient enough to play the game on their own.

3. Have students choose a partner, or assign them one, and hand out the student sheet. Groups will need two or three sheets if the sheets are not laminated.

4. Allow the students time to play several rounds of the game, and encourage them to develop a game-playing strategy to find the hurkle in the minimum number of tries.

5. Have a time of class discussion where students share any strategies they may have developed and discuss what they have learned.

Discussion

1. What was the fewest number of guesses that it took you to find the hurkle?
2. What was the greatest number of guesses?
3. What strategies did you develop for searching for the hurkle?
4. How are these strategies related to the strategy you used in *I've Got Your Number*?

Extensions

1. Change the size of the grid to 15 x 15 or 20 x 20.
2. Go to the AIMS web site and have students try our computerized version of the game. (www.AIMSedu.org)
3. Use a four quadrant grid in which to hide the hurkle.

Solutions

This is an example of how a game of *Hurkle Hide and Seek* might proceed.

The hurkle is hidden at (4, 3)

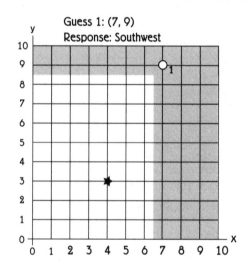

Guess 1: (7, 9)
Response: Southwest

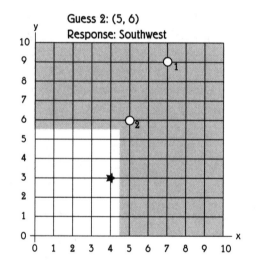

Guess 2: (5, 6)
Response: Southwest

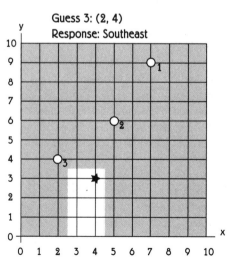

Guess 3: (2, 4)
Response: Southeast

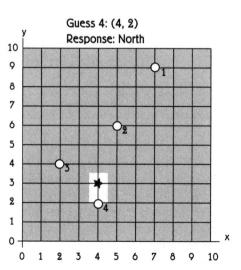

Guess 4: (4, 2)
Response: North

Guess 5: (4, 3)
Response: You found the hurkle!

Hurkle Hide and Seek

An invisible creature called a hurkle is hiding at one of the intersections of this grid. Your challenge is to find the hurkle in as few guesses as possible. To guess, give a pair of numbers. The first number comes from the x (bottom) axis and the second number comes from the y (side) axis. For each guess, you will be given a directional clue to help you find the hurkle. Good luck!

Hurkle Hide and Seek

Take turns playing *Hurkle Hide and Seek* using the grids below. Make a record of your guesses and the clues on a separate piece of paper. Try to develop a strategy to find the hurkle in as few guesses as possible.

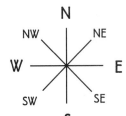

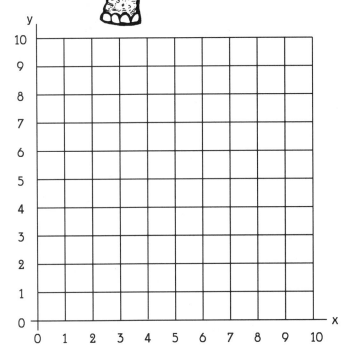

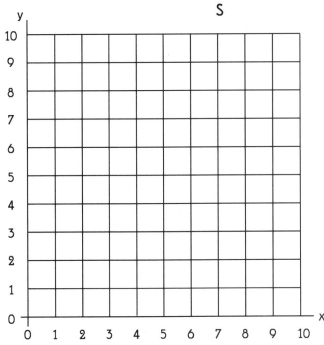

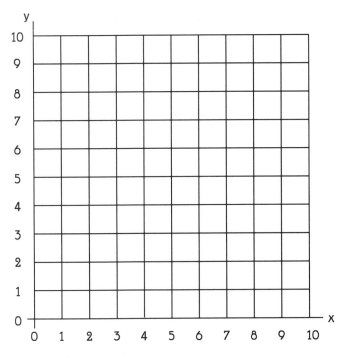

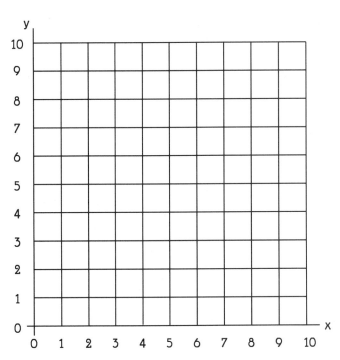

　　　© 1999 AIMS Education Foundation

Penny Patterns
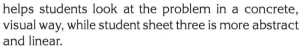

Topic
Problem solving

Key Question
How can you arrange five pennies in a five by five grid so that no two pennies are in the same row, column, or diagonal?

Focus
Students will systematically approach the problem and discover all of the possible solutions.

Guiding Document
NCTM Standards
- *Use problem solving approaches to investigate and understand mathematical content*
- *Justify answers and solution process*
- *Develop spatial sense*

Math
Math patterns
Spatial visualization

Integrated Processes
Observing
Collecting and recording data

Materials
Student sheets
Pennies (or other small objects), five per student

Background Information
This activity appears in a similar form in many recreational mathematics books; however, the focus of the problem is usually on finding one correct solution. This limited approach ignores one of the unique features of this problem—the fact that it has multiple solutions. It is the goal of *Penny Patterns* to take a broader approach to the problem by having students find *all* of the correct solutions, as well as justify their responses. When this problem is approached in a systematic way, some patterns become obvious, and it is easy to find all of the ten possible solutions. Your students will be challenged to stretch their thinking beyond just getting the "right" answer and will focus on the process more than the product.

Management
1. This problem is designed to be either open-ended or structured. If your class functions well with open-ended problems, only give them the first student sheet to work on. If your class needs more structure, give them all three student sheets. Student sheet two helps students look at the problem in a concrete, visual way, while student sheet three is more abstract and linear.
2. Note that there are 16 spaces to record solutions on the second student sheet and 12 on the third student sheet while there are only ten solutions. This has been done intentionally so students will not be able to determine the number of possible solutions from the activity pages.
3. To help your students understand the rules, it may be helpful to use a transparency of student sheet one on the overhead.
4. If pennies are unavailable, other small objects, such as beans or buttons, can be substituted.
5. An essential part of this problem is discovery. Because of this, it is important that you not tell your students that there are ten solutions. It will be more rewarding for them if they are allowed to discover this for themselves.

Procedure
1. Hand out the student sheet(s) and go over the instructions (using the overhead if desired). *Place five pennies in the grid below so that no two pennies are in the same row, column, or diagonal.* It is important that students understand that the prohibition against two pennies on a diagonal in this problem applies to *all diagonals*, not just the two corner-to-corner ones.
2. If you feel your students need some help getting started, find one or two solutions together as a class.
3. Have students work in groups, and allow them sufficient time to discover all ten solutions and formulate an argument for why they think they have found them all.
4. Close with a class discussion in which students share their solutions, how they discovered them, and their justifications for having found every possibility.

Discussion
1. How many possible solutions are there? [ten]
2. How do you know this? (See *Solutions*.)
3. What patterns do you see in the solutions? (See *Solutions*.)
4. How could you have used these patterns to discover all the possible solutions without actually trying each one?
5. Do you think you could get a solution using four pennies in a four by four square? Why or why not? [This is not possible because there are not enough diagonals—two of the pennies will always be on the same row, column or diagonal.]

Extensions

1. Have students find all possible solutions for squares larger than five by five. They will discover that it is not possible to get a solution with an even number of squares because there are not enough diagonals.

2. Have students plot the different solutions on a line graph to visually compare the patterns in a different way.

3. Group solutions with their mirror images based on a visual representation.

Solutions

These are the ten unique solutions possible with a five by five grid.

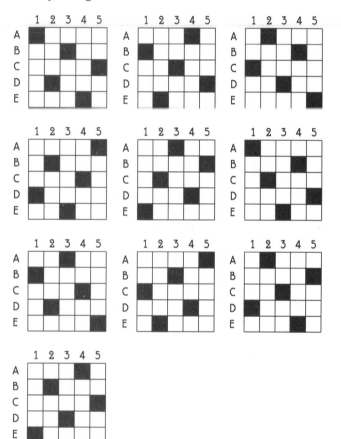

There are many patterns present in this problem. Following are a few of the many which your students may notice.

1. The ten possible solutions can be grouped into two sets of five. In the first set, the numbers always occur in the order: 1, 3, 5, 2, 4. The number corresponding with A determines where in the sequence you start, but the progression is the same. For example, one solution has (A, **1**), (B, **3**), (C, **5**), (D, **2**), (E, **4**) and another has (A, **3**), (B, **5**), (C, **2**), (D, **4**), (E, **1**). In the second set of solutions, the numbers occur in the order 1, 4, 2, 5, 3.

2. The numbers which correspond to consecutive letters must always have a difference of at least two, or the pennies will be on the same diagonal. For example, if C is 2, then B and D must be at least 4; if D is 4, then C and E cannot be 3 or 5.

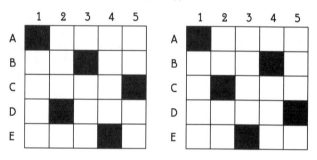

As you can see, if a penny is placed in box (C, 2), pennies cannot be placed in row C, column 2, or the two diagonals which go through (C, 2).

3. Each letter has two solutions at each number ((A, 1) occurs twice; (A, 2) occurs twice; etc.). These are the two solutions for (A, 1)).

This is the table from the third student sheet with all of the possible combinations filled in. The number of the solution is not specific to the combination—your students may have them in a different order.

Solution	(Letter, Number) Pairs used in Solution
1	(A, 1), (B, 3), (C, 5), (D, 2), (E, 4)
2	(A, 4), (B, 1), (C, 3), (D, 5), (E, 2)
3	(A, 2), (B, 4), (C, 1), (D, 3), (E, 5)
4	(A, 5), (B, 2), (C, 4), (D, 1), (E, 3)
5	(A, 3), (B, 5), (C, 2), (D, 4), (E, 1)
6	(A, 1), (B, 4), (C, 2), (D, 5), (E, 3)
7	(A, 3), (B, 1), (C, 4), (D, 2), (E, 5)
8	(A, 5), (B, 3), (C, 1), (D, 4), (E, 2)
9	(A, 2), (B, 5), (C, 3), (D, 1), (E, 4)
10	(A, 4), (B, 2), (C, 5), (D, 3), (E, 1)

Penny Patterns

Place five pennies in the grid below so that no two pennies are in the same row, column, or diagonal.

Find as many different solutions as you can and record them.

Have you found them all?

How can you be sure?

	1	2	3	4	5
A					
B					
C					
D					
E					

Penny Patterns

Record each of your unique solutions by shading in the appropriate boxes in the grids below. For example, if your solution has a penny in the upper left box, shade in that box.

What visual patterns do you notice?

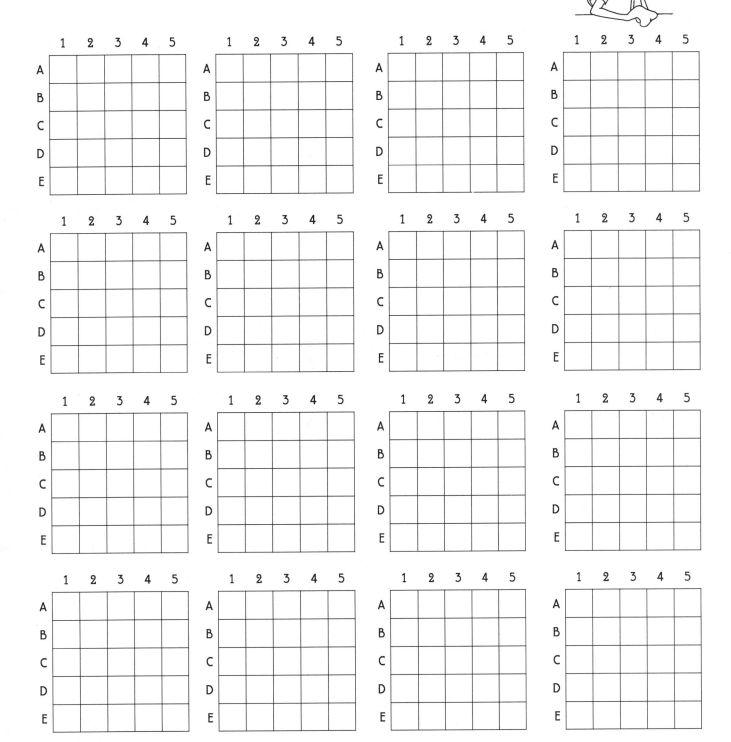

Penny Patterns

Record each of your solutions in the table below using letter and number pairs. For example, if your solution has a penny in the top right box, it would be recorded by pair (A, 5).

What patterns do you notice when recording the information this way?

Solution	(Letter, Number) Pairs used in Solution
1	(A,), (B,), (C,), (D,), (E,)
2	(A,), (B,), (C,), (D,), (E,)
3	(A,), (B,
4	

Use the space below to explain how you know you have all the possible answers.

That's *SUM* Challenge!

Topic
Numerical patterns

Key Question
What sums from one to 25 can be obtained by adding two, three, four, five, or six consecutive numbers?

Focus
Students will work together in groups to find which sums from one to 25 can be obtained by adding two, three, four, five, or six consecutive numbers. More importantly, they will discover and discuss the patterns which exist in the solutions.

Guiding Documents
Project 2061 Benchmark
- *Mathematics is the study of many kinds of patterns, including numbers and shapes and operations on them. Sometimes patterns are studied because they help to explain how the world works or how to solve practical problems, sometimes because they are interesting in themselves.*

NCTM Standards
- *Use patterns and functions to represent and solve problems*
- *Recognize, describe, extend, and create a variety of patterns*

Math
Multiple solutions
Whole number operations
Number sense and numeration
Math patterns

Integrated Processes
Observing
Inferring
Generalizing
Applying

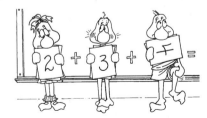

Materials
Student pages

Background Information
A wonderful principle of mathematics is that whenever numbers of any kind are arranged according to some rule, patterns emerge. These patterns range from very simple to complex, but they are always present. It is the goal of this problem to have your students discover some of these exciting patterns.

Most of the mathematics in the early elementary grades and much of the mathematics in the upper elementary deals with whole numbers. Whole numbers are defined mathematically as the set of natural numbers (also called counting numbers) $N = \{1, 2, 3, \ldots \}$ plus zero. Thus, the set of whole numbers can be denoted by $W = \{0, 1, 2, 3, \ldots\}$.

In middle school, the study of integers is a common, and often confusing, topic. The set of integers is formed by adding the negative numbers $\{-1, -2, -3, -4, \ldots\}$ to the set of whole numbers. Therefore, the set of integers can be denoted by $I = \{\ldots -3, -2, -1, 0, 1, 2, 3, \ldots\}$.

This activity, as written, has the students using whole numbers to arrive at their solutions. However, if you have an older class who has been introduced to negative numbers, using the integer set can be a powerful extension of the problem (see *Extensions*). For an explanation of integer solutions and patterns, see *Solutions*.

Management
1. The answer key is provided for you and should help you to ask leading questions which will facilitate students' pattern recognition.
2. Have students work together in small groups to solve the problem, allowing them to interact and help each other discover patterns.
3. If you have a class that functions well with open-ended problems, you can explain the problem to them and have them solve it without using the student sheets.

Procedure
1. Hand out the student sheets and review the instructions. *In this problem your group is to find every set of consecutive numbers (including zero) that can be added together to total any sum from one to 25.*
2. Allow students sufficient time to work on the problem, then regroup for a time of sharing in which you go over the answers to the questions and allow each group to show the patterns they discovered in the problem.

Discussion
Discussion should be generated by the questions given to the students on the student pages. The questions and possible answers are as follows:
1. Which of the sums from one to 25 can be obtained by adding consecutive numbers? (See *Answer Key*.)

2. Which sums cannot be obtained? [2, 4, 8, and 16]
   Optional: Is there a way to get these numbers?
   [Yes. They can be obtained using integers. (See
   Answer Key.)]
3. What patterns do you see in the completed table?
   (Have students defend their answers.)
4. What sums are obtained by adding two consecutive
   numbers? [odd numbers] Why do you think this
   happens? [Two consecutive numbers always include
   an even and an odd, and when added, they always
   produce an odd number.]
5. What sums are obtained by adding three consecutive numbers? [3, 6, 9, 12, 15, 18, 21, 24] What
   patterns do you see in these sums? [They are all
   multiples of three.]
6. What process did your group use to fill in the table?

Extensions

1. Use the set of integers instead of the whole
   number set.
2. Find the sums for the numbers from -25 to zero.
3. Find a sum for every number, from zero to 25
   even if it involves adding more than six consecutive numbers. (This requires the use of negative
   numbers).
4. Find the possible sums for zero to 25 by adding
   consecutive odd numbers.
5. Find the possible sums for zero to 25 by adding
   consecutive even numbers.

Solutions

This section lists some of the patterns that exist in
this problem, but it is by no means exhaustive. It is
hoped that your students will discover patterns that
are not listed below.

1. Only odd numbers can be obtained by adding two
   consecutive numbers.
2. Powers of two (2, 4, 8, 16, 32, etc.) cannot be
   obtained by adding positive consecutive numbers.
3. Only multiples of three (3, 6, 9, 12, etc.) can be
   obtained by adding three consecutive numbers.
4. Sums which can be made by adding four consecutive numbers are all separated by four (6, 10, 14,
   18, 22, etc.).
5. Only multiples of five (5, 10, 15, 20, 25, etc.) can
   be obtained by adding five consecutive numbers.
6. Some interesting diagonal patterns occur when you
   look at sets of consecutive solutions that begin with
   the same whole number. If you look at how many
   rows separate a solution starting with a certain
   number in one column and the solution starting with
   that same number in the next column, you will
   discover that the separation increases by one each
   time you move one column to the right. For example,
   with solutions that start with zero (beginning in the
   first column) you go over one, down two; over one,
   down three; over one, down four; etc.

An additional pattern is that as the initial number
in the solution increases, so does the initial separation. For example, solutions that start with one
begin with a difference of over one, down three;
and solutions that start with two begin with a
difference of over one, down four.

This pattern can be generalized as follows. If n is
the first number in the solution, then the number of
rows between the solution in the first column and
the solution in the second column is $n + 2$, between
the second and third column is $n + 3$, between the
third and the fourth column is $n + 4$, and so on.

Sum	Two Consecutive Numbers	Three Consecutive Numbers	Four Consecutive Numbers
0	over one		
1	0+1 → down two		
2			over one
3	1+2	0+1+2 →	
4			down three
5	2+3		
6		1+2+3	0+1+2+3
7	3+4		

7. When using integers, the same patterns that appear
   in the positive numbers, continue with the negative.
   There is a perfect symmetry of solutions above and
   below the zero, as can be see by comparing the
   answer keys for -25 to zero and zero to 25.

That's *SUM* Challenge!

In this problem your group is to find every set of consecutive numbers (including zero) that can be added together to total any sum from one to 25. For example, the sum of the four consecutive numbers *zero, one, two,* and *three* is six. We have recorded this for you in the proper box opposite *"6,"* the sum, and under "Four Consecutive Numbers." Are there any other sets of consecutive numbers that total six? If so, write them in the proper box on this same line.

See how many other series your group can find. Then answer the following questions.

1. Which of the sums from one to 25 can be obtained by adding consecutive numbers?

2. Which sums cannot be obtained?

3. What patterns do you see in the completed table?

That's *SUM* Challenge!

4. What sums are obtained by adding two consecutive numbers? Why do you think this happens?

5. What sums are obtained by adding three consecutive numbers? What patterns do you see in these sums?

6. What process did your group use to fill in the table?

That's **SUM** Challenge!

Follow the directions on the first page to complete this table.

Sum	Two Consecutive Numbers	Three Consecutive Numbers	Four Consecutive Numbers	Five Consecutive Numbers	Six Consecutive Numbers
0					
1					
2					
3					
4					
5					
6			0+1+2+3		
7					
8					
9					
10					
11					
12					
13					
14					
15					
16					
17					
18					
19					
20					
21					
22					
23					
24					
25					

That's *SUM* Challenge! Extension

Use integers (positive and negative numbers) to complete this table.

Sum	Two Consecutive Numbers	Three Consecutive Numbers	Four Consecutive Numbers	Five Consecutive Numbers	Six Consecutive Numbers
-25					
-24					
-23					
-22					
-21					
-20					
-19					
-18					
-17					
-16					
-15					
-14					
-13					
-12					
-11					
-10					
-9					
-8					
-7					
-6					
-5					
-4					
-3					
-2					
-1					
0					

That's *SUM* Challenge!

Answer Key for zero to 25

Integer solutions (in parentheses) are optional.

Sum	Two Consecutive Numbers	Three Consecutive Numbers	Four Consecutive Numbers	Five Consecutive Numbers	Six Consecutive Numbers
0		(-1+0+1)		(-2+-1+0+1+2)	
1	0+1				
2			(-1+0+1+2)		
3	1+2	0+1+2			(-2+-1+0+1+2+3)
4					
5	2+3			(-1+0+1+2+3)	
6		1+2+3	0+1+2+3		
7	3+4				
8					
9	4+5	2+3+4			(-1+0+1+2+3+4)
10			1+2+3+4	0+1+2+3+4	
11	5+6				
12		3+4+5			
13	6+7				
14			2+3+4+5		
15	7+8	4+5+6		1+2+3+4+5	0+1+2+3+4+5
16					
17	8+9				
18		5+6+7	3+4+5+6		
19	9+10				
20				2+3+4+5+6	
21	10+11	6+7+8			1+2+3+4+5+6
22			4+5+6+7		
23	11+12				
24		7+8+9			
25	12+13			3+4+5+6+7	

That's *SUM* Challenge!

Answer Key for -25 to zero

Sum	Two Consecutive Numbers	Three Consecutive Numbers	Four Consecutive Numbers	Five Consecutive Numbers	Six Consecutive Numbers
-25	(-13+-12)			(-7+-6+-5+-4+-3)	
-24		(-10+-9+-8)			
-23	(-12+-11)				
-22			(-7+-6+-5+-4)		
-21	(-11+-10)	(-9+-8+-7)			(-6+-5+-4+-3+-2+-1)
-20				(-6+-5+-4+-3+-2)	
-19	(-10+-9)				
-18		(-8+-7+-6)	(-6+-5+-4+-3)		
-17	(-9+-8)				
-16					
-15	(-8+-7)	(-7+-6+-4)		(-5+-4+-3+-2+-1)	(-5+-4+-3+-2+-1+0)
-14			(-5+-4+-3+-2)		
-13	(-7+-6)				
-12		(-6+-5+-4)			
-11	(-6+-5)				
-10			(-4+-3+-2+-1)	(-4+-3+-2+-1+0)	
-9	(-5+-4)	(-4+-3+-2)			(-4+-3+-2+-1+0+1)
-8					
-7	(-4+-3)				
-6		(-3+-2+-1)	(-3+-2+-1+0)		
-5	(-3+-2)			(-3+-2+-1+0+1)	
-4					
-3	(-2+-1)	(-2+-1+0)			(-3+-2+-1+0+1+2)
-2			(-2+-1+0+1)		
-1	(-1+0)				
0		(-1+0+1)		(-2+-1+0+1+2)	

Balance ? Baffier ? ? ? ?

Topic
Problem Solving

Key Question
Using only a balance, how can you find the canister that is lighter than the others in the fewest tries?

Focus
Students will be challenged to discover which of eight identical-looking canisters has less mass than the others by using a balance. The goal is for them to discover a way to consistently do this in only two trials.

Guiding Document
NCTM Standards
- *Use models, known facts, properties and relationships to explain their thinking*
- *Justify answers and solution processes*
- *Appreciate the pervasive use and power of reasoning as a part of mathematics*

Math
Equalities and inequalities
Logical thinking

Integrated Processes
Observing
Comparing and contrasting
Generalizing
Applying

Materials
Balances, one per group
Film canisters, eight per group (see *Management*)
Identical objects such as Friendly Bears (see *Management 1*)
Student sheets

Background Information
This problem is a modification of a classic thought problem in mathematics. The problem is usually presented as follows:

There are eight gold coins, all of which look identical. Seven of the coins are pure gold and have the same mass, but one is an alloy and has a mass less than that of the others. Can you use a balance to find the light coin in only two trials every time?

The puzzle in its original form is quite challenging, even for most adults. Yet, by modifying the problem slightly and using real objects, it can be solved by elementary-school children. In the most challenging part of this problem, students will discover a way to find the lighter canister by using the balance only twice ("two trials"). This is easy to do by chance, but there is also a way that they are guaranteed to find the lighter canister every time.

Management
1. For each group you will need to have eight identical-looking film canisters. Seven of the canisters must be filled with the same number of identical objects (such as plastic chips or Friendly Bears). Put one or two fewer objects in the eighth canister, so that there is a measurable difference between its mass and that of the other seven. These canisters should not be the kind made of translucent plastic, or students will be able to tell by looking at them which of the canisters has fewer objects. Many film processors will donate canisters.
2. When students begin *Part Two* of the problem, assure them that it is possible to find the light canister in just two trials *every time*. Students will quickly realize that if they get lucky and pick the light canister first, it can be found in one trial, however, this will not work every time.

Procedure
1. Divide students into groups and give each group a balance and eight film canisters.
2. Distribute the first student sheet for *Part 1* and go over the instructions. *You have been given eight small canisters. All have the same mass except for one. Without opening the canisters, use the balance to find the canister that is lighter than the others in a way that will work every time.*
3. Give the groups time to find the light canister in a way that will work every time, then distribute the second student sheet for *Part 2* and go over the instructions. *See if you can discover a way to find the light canister in exactly three trials every time. Once you have done that, see if you can find it in exactly two trials every time.*
4. Give enough time for every group to find the light canister in three trials, and for at least one group to find the light canister in two trials every time.
5. Have a time of class discussion where groups share the techniques they used to solve the problem and the process they went through to discover those techniques. If not all groups discover the two-trials solution, have one of the groups that did show the rest of the class and explain the process.

Discussion

1. How many trials did it take you to solve the problem the first time?
2. Is it possible to find the light canister in one trial? [Yes.]
3. Why doesn't this work every time? [It depends on chance.]
4. How many different ways do you think there are to find the light canister in three trials? (See *Solutions*.)
5. What are the possible scenarios for finding the light canister in two trials every time? (See *Solutions*.)

Extensions

1. Give the students 10 canisters, and challenge them to find the light canister in only three trials every time. This can be done in two different ways.
2. Give the students eight canisters with the instructions to find the canister that is different in the fewest trials, *without knowing whether the different canister is heavier or lighter than the others.*
3. Find the minimum number of trials for any number of canisters and express this algebraically.

Solutions

The methods listed below are only for finding the lighter canister in two and three trials. There are many ways to find the lighter canister in three trials, and it is hoped that during the discovery process, your students will discover some methods that are not listed here.

*Methods for finding the light canister in **three** trials every time:*

Method One

1. Put four of the canisters on the balance, two on each side.
2. If the pans are even, go to #3. If they are uneven, go to #4.
3. Put those four canisters aside, and place the remaining four on the balance, two on each side.
4. Put the two heavy canisters aside, and place one canister from the lighter pair on each side of the balance.
5. Whichever is lighter is the canister you are looking for.

Method Two

1. Place four canisters on each side of the balance.
2. Put the heavier four canisters aside.
3. Divide the four lighter canisters in half, placing two on each side of the balance.
4. Put the heavier two canisters aside and place one canister from the lighter pair on each side of the balance.
5. Whichever is lighter is the canister you are looking for.

Method Three

1. Place two canisters on the balance, one on each side. If the pans are even, go to #2. If they are uneven, go to #5.
2. Put the first two canisters aside. Take four of the remaining six canisters and place two on each side of the balance. If the pans are even, go to #3. If they are uneven, go to #4.
3. Put the second four canisters aside. Place the remaining two canisters on the balance, one on each side, go to #5.
4. Put the heavier two canisters aside. Place one of the remaining pair on each side of the balance.
5. Whichever is lighter is the canister you are looking for.

*Method for finding the light canister in **two** trials every time:*

1. Place six of the eight canisters on the balance, three on each side. If the pans are even, go to #2. If they are uneven, go to #3.
2. Put the first six canisters aside. Place the remaining two canisters on the balance. Whichever is lighter is the canister you are looking for.
3. Put the heavier three canisters aside. Of the remaining three lighter canisters, put one aside. Place the remaining two canisters on the balance, one on each side. If they are even, go to #4. If they are uneven, the lighter canister is the one you are looking for.
4. The canister you set aside in step #3 is the one you are looking for.

Balance Baffler

Part 1

You have been given eight small canisters. All have the same mass except one. Without opening the canisters, use the balance to find the canister that has less mass in a way that will work every time. Record your method in the box below using words and/or pictures.

I found the light canister in _____ trials.
This is how.

Balance ? Baffler ?

Part 2

This part has two challenges. In the *Warm-up Challenge*, see if you can discover a way to find the light canister in exactly three trials every time. In the *Big Balance Baffler Challenge*, see if you can find it in exactly two trials every time. Record your methods in the boxes using words and/or pictures.

Warm-up Challenge

This is how I can find the light canister in exactly three trials every time.

Big Balance Baffler Challenge

This is how I can find the light canister in exactly two trials every time.

Desert Crossings

Topic
Problem solving

Key Question
What is the maximum number of watermelons you can get to market?

Focus
Students will have to employ creative thinking and problem solving in order to solve a seemingly impossible problem.

Guiding Documents
Project 2061 Benchmarks
- *Make sketches to aid in explaining procedures or ideas.*
- *Mathematical ideas can be represented concretely, graphically, and symbolically.*

NCTM Standards
- *Use problem-solving approaches to investigate and understand mathematical content*
- *Develop and apply a variety of strategies to solve problems, with emphasis on multistep and nonroutine problems*

Math
Whole number operations
Counting
One-to-one correspondence

Integrated Processes
Observing
Collecting and recording data
Inferring
Applying

Materials
Student sheet
Manipulatives, optional (see *Management 4*)

Background Information
Some problems in recreational mathematics seem, at first glance, impossible to solve. Once some key insight is made, however, these problems "open up" and can be solved using traditional mathematics. The activity presented here is one of these problems.

Some people decry these types of problems as "tricks" which have no place in the classroom. However, if students are able to uncover the trick as part of the problem-solving process, they gain a tremendous sense of power and satisfaction.

Desert Crossings actually has some ties to real-life problems. In World War II both the Allied and Axis armies crossed large expanses of the Sahara Desert in North Africa where no fuel, water, food, or other supplies were available. How did the armies do this when they were not able to carry enough supplies with them to make the crossing in a single trip? Thinking about this question may give you the insight needed to solve *Desert Crossings*. Please try to solve this problem yourself before assigning it to your students.

Management
1. It is important to note that this problem has multiple solutions, with one "best" answer. It is possible to get as many as eight melons to market, but *all* answers between one and eight should be accepted.
2. Emphasize to your students that it is not necessary to break the rules of the problem to arrive at a solution. While your students may generate some creative solutions which can give you wonderful insights into their thought processes, these answers do not uncover the rich mathematics inherent in the problem. Therefore, "Build a wheelbarrow and take all 45 melons at once. Eat 15 along the way, getting 30 to the market." is an interesting, but unacceptable response.
3. There is a critical leap of insight which students must make in order to solve this problem. It is essential that they be allowed to make this discovery for themselves. If students are completely stuck, some general hints may be given, such as, "Notice the phrasing of the problem: for each kilometer you walk *in either direction...*"
4. Some students may find it helpful to use manipulatives to represent the melons. You may want to have beans or some other small items available for this purpose.

Procedure
1. Distribute the student sheet and explain the directions. *You live in a desert oasis and grow miniature watermelons that are worth a great*

deal of money, if you can get them to the market 15 kilometers away across the desert. Your harvest this year is 45 melons, but you have no way to get them to the market except to carry them across the desert. You have a backpack that holds up to 15 melons, the maximum number that you can carry at a time. To walk across the desert, you need a certain amount of fluid and nourishment which is supplied by the melons you carry. For each kilometer you walk (in either direction), one melon must be eaten. Your challenge is to find a way to get as many melons as possible to market. (Inform students that they do not need to break the rules to solve the puzzle.)

2. Give students adequate time to discover ways to get one or more melons to market.
3. After students have had time to solve the puzzle at least one way, have them share the methods they used to get their melons to market. If no student is able to get eight melons to market, see if you can come up with this solution as a class.

Discussion

1. Why did this problem seem impossible at first? [You can only carry 15 melons, and it is 15 km to market. Since you have to eat one melon per kilometer, it seems impossible.]
2. What did you need to do in order to get one or more melons to market? (See *Solutions*.)
3. How many melons were you able to get to market?
4. How did you reach this solution?
5. What method did you use to keep track of how many melons you had eaten along the way? [Various. Manipulatives, drawing a picture, writing it down, etc.]
6. What do you think is the most number of melons it is possible to get to market? [eight]
7. Why can't you get more than eight? (See *Solutions*.)

Extensions

1. Find the maximum number of melons possible if you have a harvest of 90 watermelons, can carry 30 at a time, and have 30 kilometers to travel.
2. Find the maximum number of melons you can get to market if you only have to eat one for every two kilometers you travel in either direction.

3. Find the maximum number of melons you can get to market if the market is 20 kilometers away instead of only 15.
4. Find the furthest distance it is possible to be from the market and still get at least one watermelon there (given a harvest of 45 and the ability to carry 15 watermelons at a time).

Solutions

There are three steps which are necessary to solve this problem completely. The first is the leap of insight that you can put down some of the watermelons at various points along the way and pick them up at another time. Once this has been realized, the second step of trial and error can begin. This step involves trying different ways to get one or more melons to market. The third and final step is the realization that two things are necessary in order to get the maximum number of melons to market. First, you must always fill your backpack to capacity, and second, you must never leave any watermelons behind at the oasis or any staging area after leaving these points for the last time.

Only the most profitable solution, which was obtained by working backwards, is recorded below. It is hoped that your students will have obtained many of the other possible solutions, which can be checked for accuracy by simple addition and subtraction.

With a harvest of 45 melons, and 15 kilometers to travel, it is possible to get a maximum of eight melons to market. In order to do this, you must get 15 melons to the eight-kilometer point. From there you can eat one melon per kilometer and travel the remaining seven kilometers, leaving you with eight melons to sell. In order to get 15 melons to the eight-kilometer point, you must get 30 melons to the three-kilometer point.

The logic used to obtain this solution was to find the first point to which you could get (three-kilometer) and have exactly 30 melons, with none left at the oasis. This way you could fill the backpack to capacity twice and not leave any behind. The next step was to get to a second point (eight-kilometer) where you would have exactly 15 melons, and only a few kilometers left to travel. This solution, which is one of several that gets eight to market, is illustrated below.

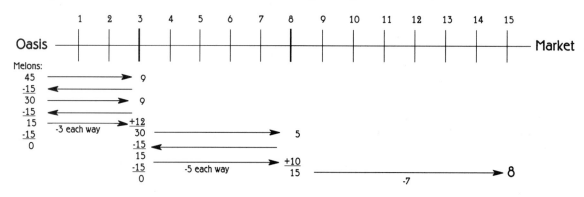

© 1999 AIMS Education Foundation

Desert Crossings

You live in a desert oasis and grow miniature watermelons that are worth a great deal of money, if you can get them to the market 15 kilometers away across the desert. Your harvest this year is 45 melons, but you have no way to get them to the market, except to carry them across the desert. You have a backpack that holds up to 15 melons, the maximum number that you can carry at a time. To walk across the desert, you need a certain amount of fluid and nourishment which is supplied by the melons you carry. For each kilometer you walk (in either direction), one melon must be eaten.

Your challenge is to find a way to get as many melons as possible to market.

CUBE CONSTRUCTION

Topic
Soma Cubes

Key Question
How many unique arrangements can you make using two to four wooden blocks when at least one face of each block must touch the face of another block?

Focus
Students will discover and construct the seven irregular shapes which compose a Soma Cube.

Guiding Document
NCTM Standard
* *Explore transformations of geometric figures*

Math
Geometry and spatial sense

Integrated Processes
Observing
Classifying

Materials
Student sheets
White glue
Wax paper
Wooden cubes, 27 per student (see *Management*)

Background Information
This activity has students construct the pieces which make up a Soma Cube. The Soma Cube was invented in 1936 by Piet Hein, a Danish scientist, mathematician, architect, puzzle inventor, and poet. Martin Gardner tells the story of this puzzle's discovery in the book, *The 2nd SCIENTIFIC AMERICAN Book of Mathematical Puzzles & Diversions*:

> Piet Hein conceived of the Soma Cube during a lecture on quantum physics by Werner Heisenberg. While the noted German physicist was speaking of a space sliced into cubes, Piet Hein's supple imagination caught a fleeting glimpse of the following curious geometrical theorem. If you take all the irregular shapes that can be formed by combining no more than four cubes, all the same size and joined at their faces, these shapes can be put together to form a larger cube (p. 66).

Hein named the puzzle after the drug in Huxley's *Brave New World* which created a dreamlike trance in its users. While he invented many other puzzles, the Soma Cube is the most widely known. The focus of this activity is on the construction of the Soma Cube pieces, using the same process which Hein did when he originally conceived them.

Management
1. *Cube Construction* and the next activity, *Record Making Cubes*, are designed to be done together since both deal with the Soma Cube, a fascinating and versatile wooden puzzle. *Cube Construction* needs to be done first, since students build the pieces for the puzzle in the activity. These two Soma Cube activities work best if each student has his or her own puzzle. The Soma Cube is so motivating for students, that the small investment required to buy the cubes for your students is well worth it.
2. AIMS sells bags of 500 two-centimeter wooden cubes (order #1939). Cubes may also be available from some educational suppliers. If you have access to a table saw, cubes can also be cut from pieces of 1" x 1" x 8' lumber (really 3/4" x 3/4" x 8').
3. When students begin the second half of the activity and start gluing their cubes together, it is important that they do not use too much glue. *If it is used sparingly*, the white glue found in most classrooms works fine for joining the cubes. Using too much glue significantly increases the drying time and also increases the chance that the cubes will slide before the glue sets. When this happens, the cubes don't end up joined face to face, and the puzzle piece is ruined.
4. Put down waxed paper in the work area so that the blocks don't stick to the surface beneath.
5. If you are worried about the students having the wrong combinations for the pieces, you can hand out the *Solutions* page, which pictures the seven irregular pieces. Another option is to make an overhead transparency of this page to put up for the class. This page should not be given to students until *after* they have come up with the irregular shapes on their own.

Procedure
1. Hand out the student sheets and go over the instructions for the first part of the activity. *The rule for any arrangement is that each cube in an arrangement must touch at least one other cube face to face. The task for this part of the activity is to try to find all the unique arrangements for four or fewer cubes. For an arrangement to be unique,*

it must differ from other arrangements even when it is rotated and/or flipped.

2. Divide the students into groups and give each group enough cubes (40) so that they can build all 11 of the unique arrangements possible using two to four cubes.

3. Once all of the groups are done, have students share the arrangements they discovered, making sure all 11 arrangements are mentioned.

4. Have each group sort the 11 arrangements into two sets: those that are regular (rectangular) and those that are irregular (non-rectangular). If this process is done correctly, the seven irregular arrangements (one with three cubes and six with four cubes) are the Soma Cube pieces.

5. Once the pieces have been sorted, have the students fill in the information on the student sheet. (An extra row has been added to the table for those wishing to do *Extension* 3. If *Extension* 3 is not done, only the first three rows of chart will be completed.)

6. At this point the irregular pieces can be glued together to create the seven puzzle pieces for the Soma Cube.

Discussion

1. Why can there only be one unique arrangement using two cubes? [There is only one way two cubes can be joined so that they touch each other face to face.]

2. What things do you notice in the table you filled out? [Number of cubes in arrangement x Total number of arrangements = Total number of cubes in arrangements]

3. Did you have a hard time coming up with all of the unique arrangements for four cubes? Why or why not?

Extensions

1. Have students sort the arrangements in other ways; for example, by those that stick up and those that are flat.

2. Find the difference between the number of cubes in the irregular arrangements and the number of cubes in the regular arrangements.

3. Find the number of unique arrangements that can be made using five blocks. Since there are 29 arrangements, you will need a large supply of blocks for this (see *Solutions*).

4. Have students calculate and compare the surface area of the different unique arrangements for two, three, and four cubes.

5. In addition to gluing the irregular shapes together, glue the regular shapes together. When these pieces are added to the original Soma Cube pieces, it is possible to form a 2 x 2 x 10 rectangular prism and a 2 x 4 x 5 rectangular prism.

Solutions

The first solution sheet shows the unique irregular arrangements for two to four cubes which are glued together to form the Soma Cube pieces and the four regular arrangements which are not. If necessary, give this sheet to your class *after* they have found their arrangements to double check them before they start to glue them together. The second solution sheet shows the 29 unique irregular arrangements for five blocks as mentioned in *Extension 3*.

This is the table from the student sheet with the correct values filled in. The answers for five cubes have been included for those who use *Extension 3*.

Number of cubes in arrangement	Number of rectangular arrangements	Number of non-rectangular arrangements	Total number of arrangements	Total number of cubes in arrangements
2	1	0	1	2
3	1	1	2	6
4	2	6	8	32
5	1	28	29	145

CUBE CONSTRUCTION

Unique Arrangements for Four or Fewer Cubes

The seven irregular arrangements which should be glued together:

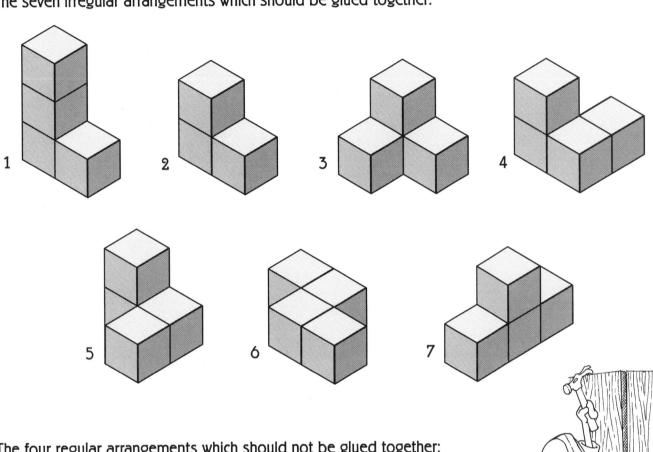

The four regular arrangements which should not be glued together:

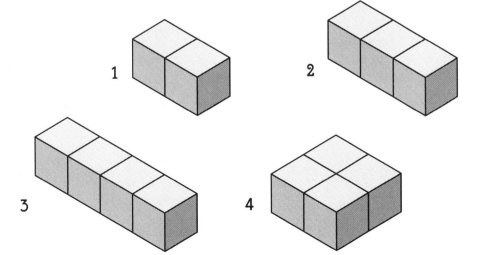

CUBE CONSTRUCTION

Unique Arrangements for Five Cubes

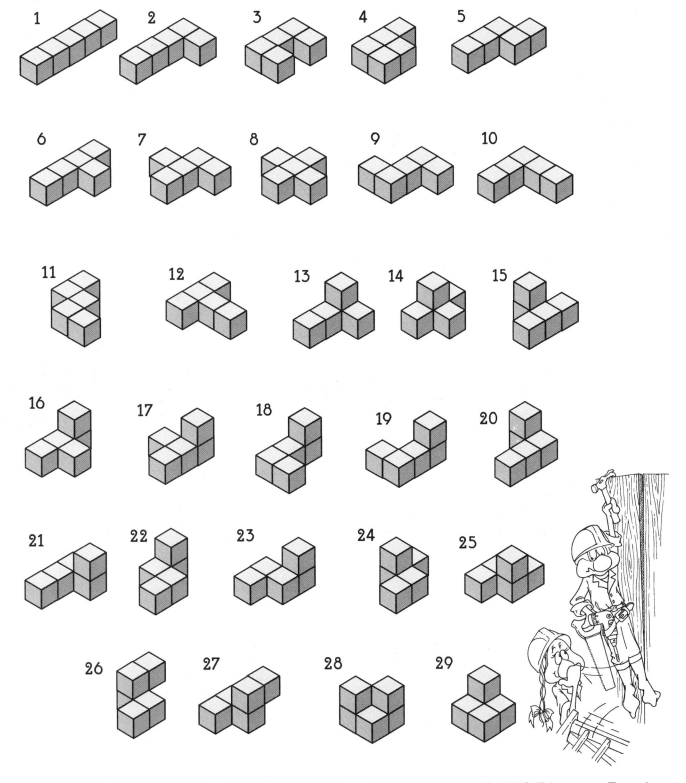

CUBE CONSTRUCTION

See how many unique arrangements of two, three, or four cubes you can make following these rules:

- Each cube in an arrangement must touch at least one other cube face to face.

- To be unique, each arrangement must be different from other arrangements even after it is flipped and/or rotated.

After building your arrangements, sort them into regular (rectangular) and irregular (non-rectangular) shapes. Then fill in the information in the chart below.

Number of cubes in arrangement	Number of rectangular arrangements	Number of non-rectangular arrangements	Total number of arrangements	Total number of cubes in arrangements

Check with your teacher to make sure you have found all the unique irregular arrangements, then glue each irregular arrangement together.

Record-Making CUBES

Topic
Soma Cubes, divergent thinking

Key Question
What are all the ways you can think of to record your solution for the Soma Cube?

Focus
Students will use divergent thinking as they record their Soma Cube solution in as many ways as possible.

Guiding Document
NCTM Standards
- *Relate physical materials, pictures, and diagrams to mathematical ideas*
- *Visualize and represent geometric figures with special attention to developing spatial sense*
- *Represent and solve problems using geometric models*

Math
Geometry and spatial sense

Integrated Processes
Observing
Collecting and recording data
Applying

Materials
Soma Cubes
Student sheets
Other materials will vary from group to group
   rulers
   colored pencils
   scissors
   scratch paper

Background Information
This activity is designed to follow *Cube Constructions* because it makes use of the Soma Cube puzzle pieces students constructed in that activity. In *Record-Making Cubes*, students will record their solution(s) for the Soma Cube in multiple ways. Since there are 240 unique ways to build a cube using the seven puzzle pieces, it is unlikely that students will find more than a fraction of the possible solutions. This is not a problem since the emphasis in this activity is not on finding multiple solutions, but rather on finding multiple ways to record a given solution.

The task of showing how the cube was built is not an easy one since it is difficult to record three-dimensional solutions using a two-dimensional medium like paper. Finding multiple ways to do this will require persistence, creativity, and divergent thinking on the part of students and lots of encouragement on the part of the teacher.

Management
1. If you do not plan to do this activity as a follow-up to *Cube Constructions,* you will need to provide a Soma Cube for each student in the class. If there are not enough Soma Cubes for each student, one per group will work.
2. Because this activity asks students to develop as many ways to record their solutions as possible, the materials used can vary widely. Included with the student sheets are an isometric dot grid and two regular grids. These are not the only materials which your students can use to record their Soma Cube solutions, but provide a starting place. Other items to have on hand include colored pencils, rulers, scissors, scratch paper, and any other items which your students might want to use to make their records.
3. Students should work in groups on this activity. However, encourage each student to record a different solution from the other members of the group, even if they are all using the same recording technique. Since there are 240 solutions for the Soma Cube, it should not be too difficult for each student to find a unique solution to record.
4. This activity will require facilitation as it is very open-ended. Students will need encouragement to be creative in their thinking and recording processes. Be sure you have plenty of copies of the graph paper and isometric dot paper for students to use if they desire.
5. Isometric dot paper is a very effective way to draw three-dimensional shapes, but it can be difficult to use at first. You may want to practice drawing some shapes yourself before you do this activity with your class so that you can assist any students who may have trouble with it.

Procedure
1. Hand out student sheet one and Soma Cubes (if necessary) and go over the instructions. *Try to build each of the shapes pictured using only two of your Soma Cube pieces. Once you have found*

a solution, make a record of it by drawing a picture in the space below. Your picture should clearly show which two pieces you used, and how you put them together. The first page can be done alone, or in groups.

2. When students have completed the warm-up, distribute student sheet two. Have students get into groups if they are not already. Explain the task, and encourage them to work together as a group to think of various ways to record their solutions. Remind students that everyone should try to find a different solution to record.

3. You can end the activity after student sheet two, or you can continue to student sheet three, which is simply an extension of the problem using shapes other than a cube.

4. Close with a time of class discussion and sharing. Have the different groups share their methods of recording solutions and the solutions that they found.

Discussion

1. How many different recording techniques did your group come up with?
2. Which method do you think is the best? Why?
3. Which method was the easiest for you?
4. What was the hardest thing about this activity for you?
5. What did you learn from this activity?

Extensions

1. Have students make their own unique shapes and challenge their classmates to recreate them.
2. As a class, see how many of the 240 different Soma Cube solutions you can discover.
3. Assign each group a few of the shapes on page four, and try to get a solution for each one. These can be left intact and used for a Soma Cube display in your classroom.

Solutions

There are numerous methods for recording solutions for the Soma Cube. Some of these methods are described below. Hopefully your students will discover some additional ways which are not listed here.

1. Using the isometric dot grid, make an expanded drawing that shows each piece and how it fits with the others.

the examples below the pieces have been numbered as shown

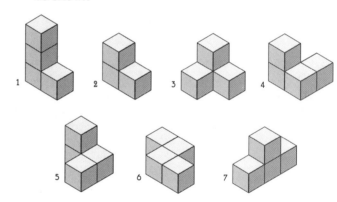

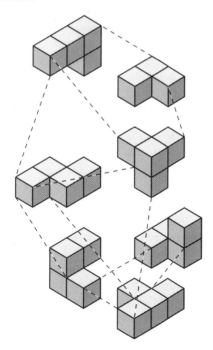

Note: The following methods require that the seven puzzle pieces be differentiated in some manner. This can be done by coloring each one a different color, or by numbering or lettering the pieces. In

2. Using the isometric dot grid, draw two 3 x 3 x 3 cubes. Number each of the squares to correspond with the piece that would go there. Because only three faces of a cube are visible in an isometric dot drawing, it is necessary to draw two views of the cube in order to see all of the faces.

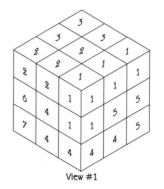

View #1

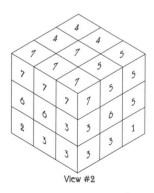

View #2

3. Using the grid paper, make a drawing of each of the six faces of the cube. Number the squares on each face to show the pieces used.

4. On the grid paper, make a record of each of the three layers of the cube, again using colors or numbers to differentiate between pieces.

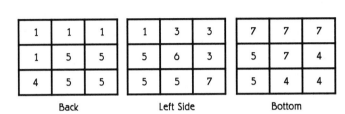

1	1	1
3	2	2
3	3	2

Top

3	3	2
3	6	6
7	7	7

Front

2	2	1
6	2	1
7	4	4

Right Side

1	1	1
3	2	2
3	3	2

Top Layer

5	5	1
6	6	4
3	6	6

Middle Layer

5	4	4
5	7	7
7	7	7

Bottom Layer

1	1	1
1	5	5
4	5	5

Back

1	3	3
5	6	3
5	5	7

Left Side

7	7	7
5	7	4
5	4	4

Bottom

Record-Making

Warm-up

Below are several shapes that can be made using only two of your Soma cube pieces. Try to build each one. When you have a solution, make a record of that solution by drawing a picture showing the pieces you used and how you put them together. For some of the shapes there is more than one solution—see if you can find them all. You can use the back of the paper if necessary.

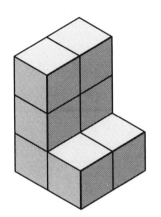 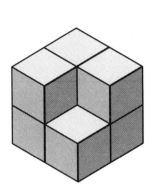 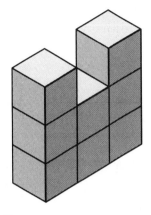 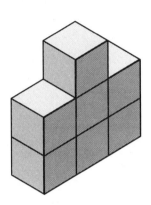

My Solutions:

Record-Making

The Challenge

Now that you have completed the warm-up, you are ready to move on to the real challenge. Using your Soma cube pieces, form a 3 x 3 x 3 cube. It should look like this:

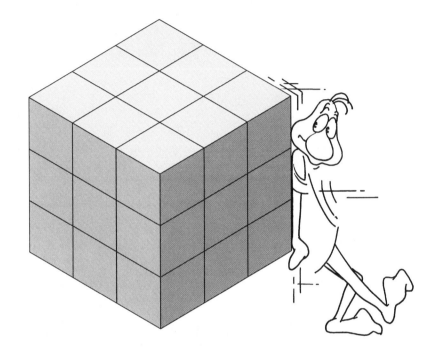

Don't worry, there are 240 different solutions, so keep trying until you get one!

Once you have a solution, the challenge is to make a record of that solution *in as many different ways as possible*. One way is to do what you did for the warm-up and draw a picture, but there are other ways. Your teacher has some grid paper and dot paper that may help you. The goal is to make each record of your solution clear enough so that anyone can look at what you have done and build the cube using the pieces the same way you did.

Record-Making

Extra Challenge

Now that you have found a solution for a Soma cube and developed several ways to record that solution, try to make some of the shapes shown below. Use one of the methods that you developed to record your solutions.

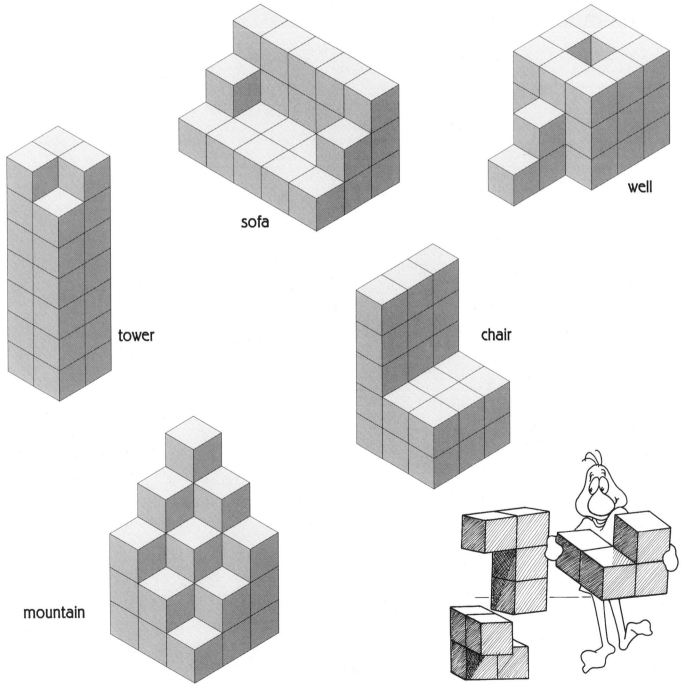

sofa

well

tower

chair

mountain

Record-Making

Extension #4

Below are some more shapes which can be made using the seven Soma cube pieces. Assign a few of these shapes to each group and try to get a solution for each one.

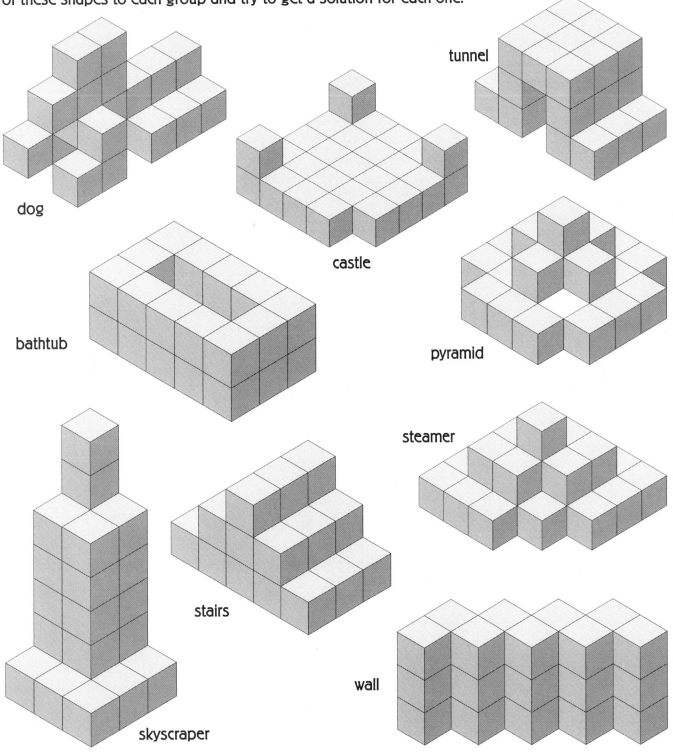

dog

castle

tunnel

bathtub

pyramid

steamer

skyscraper

stairs

wall

Centimeter Isometric Dot Grid

Spinning Sums

Topic
Probability

Key Question
What sum is most likely to occur when adding the numbers from a single spin of two zero-to-nine spinners?

Focus
Students will make a guess as to which sum is most likely to be obtained when adding the numbers from a single spin on two zero-to-nine spinners and then do an investigation to find the most common sum. They will also explore the concept of probability by finding the theoretical and experimental probabilities for each sum.

Guiding Document
NCTM Standards
- *Explore concepts of chance*
- *Make predictions that are based on experimental or theoretical probabilities*
- *Appreciate the power of using a probability model by comparing experimental results with mathematical expectations*

Math
Probability
Math patterns

Integrated Processes
Observing
Predicting
Collecting and recording data
Interpreting data
Generalizing
Applying

Materials
Student sheets
Paper clips
Paper fasteners, optional

Background Information
Spinning Sums is an activity that involves probability. Probability is the branch of mathematics that deals with the mathematical likelihood of certain events occurring. Probabilities are ratios expressed as fractions, decimals, or percents. These ratios are determined by considering the results of experiments in which *outcomes* are observed.

The set of all possible outcomes for an experiment is called the *sample space*. For example, if two coins are tossed, the sample space (which counts heads and tails) is all the possible outcomes: S = {HH, HT, TH, TT}. It is important to note that in this example, HT is a different outcome from TH.

Any subset of the sample space is an *event*. In the above example an outcome of two heads is an event.

Probabilities are determined either *experimentally* or *theoretically*. When a probability is found by observing the outcomes of an experiment, like tossing two coins, experimental probability is being used. When a probability is found by considering the outcomes of an experiment under ideal conditions, without actually doing the experiment, *theoretical probability* is being used.

In *Spinning Sums*, students will engage in experimental probability. They will spin two zero-to-nine spinners 100 times and record the sums. Since there are 100 possible outcomes in the sample space (see *Solutions*), the probability of each event (sum) can be expressed as a fraction with a denominator of 100. For example, if students get three sums of 17 out of the 100 spins the experimental probability would be 3/100. This can be written as P(17) = 3/100. It is important to note that experimental probabilities are often not the same as the theoretical probabilities. In the above example, the theoretical probability of getting a 17 is two chances out of a hundred, P(17) = 2/100, since there are only two ways out of the 100 possible outcomes to get an event of 17: eight on the first spinner and nine on the second or nine on the first spinner and eight on the second.

While this lesson does not have students working directly with theoretical probabilities, students should understand that it is more likely to get a sum of nine than a sum of any other number since there are more possible ways to get a nine than any other sum.

Management
1. The spinners needed for this problem can be constructed in more than one way. The easiest way is to have students use a pencil point to hold a paper clip at the center of the circle while giving the paper clip a flick with their finger. Another option is to use paper fasteners to hold the paper clips to the spinners. If this option is used, make sure that the paper clips spin freely.
2. The ideal group size for this activity is four students since there are four tasks that must be done when

collecting data. Two students spin the spinners to generate the sums. One student keeps a tally of the pairs of spins so the group knows when they have gotten 100 sums. One student makes a record of each sum by putting an X in the appropriate box on the bar graph. Make sure students understand that they are recording the sum of *both* spins and not each individual spin on the bar graph. There should be exactly 100 Xs on the graph at the end of the data-collection time. The graph at the end of this text is an example of one group's results when doing this activity.

3. For younger students who are not able to formally deal with probability concepts, only use the first three student sheets. This will allow them to see the reason that certain sums are more likely without getting into a formal discussion of probability. For older or more advanced students, all five student sheets can be used.

4. Student sheet four examines probability by having students compare the theoretical and experimental probability for each sum. This can be a difficult task for some students, especially if they have never been exposed to probability before. You may need to spend some time going over the following concepts (which are explained in more detail in the *Background Information* section) before having students attempt this sheet.

The theoretical probability of each sum reflects the number of times that sum is possible in comparison to the total number of combinations possible for all of the sums. Students will find this number using the information on student sheet three.

The experimental probability of each sum will be different from group to group because it reflects how many times a group actually got that sum in comparison to the total number of sums. Students will find their experimental probabilities using the information on student sheet two.

Finally, students will need to learn the proper notation for probability equations. The example given on the student page is for rolling a pair of dice. The probability of getting a sum of two when you roll a pair of dice is one out of 36. This is written: $P(2) = 1/36$.

Procedure

1. Hand out student sheets one and two and go over the instructions. *Find all of the possible sums that can occur when the two spinners are spun. Predict which of these sums is most likely to occur, and write down why you think so. In your groups, spin the spinners 100 times. Record each sum by putting an X in the appropriate box on the bar graph.*

2. Have students get into their groups and hand out the paper clips (and paper fasteners, if desired). Make sure that all students understand how to

operate their spinners correctly. A spinner which is used improperly can lead to inaccurate results.

3. Once the groups have made their predictions and answered the questions on student sheet one, have them divide the responsibilities among group members and carry out the investigation.

4. As groups finish, hand out sheets three, four, and five so that students can begin their study of probability. Be sure that students understand the concepts they are dealing with before they begin this section. The third page has students look at all of the possible combinations for each sum, and the fourth page has them determine the theoretical and experimental probability for each sum.

4. After students have finished the experiment, regroup for a time of class discussion where students share their predictions and results as well as the discoveries they made while doing this problem.

Discussion

1. What was your original prediction for the most likely sum? Why?
2. What sum did you actually get the most often? [eight, nine, or ten in most cases]
3. Why do you think this is? [These sums are produced by the most possible combinations.]
4. What would be the most likely sum if you only had the numbers one to five on the spinners? [six] ...two to ten? [12]
5. What if one of the sections on the spinner was bigger than the others? How would that affect the probability of getting certain sums? [It would increase the probability of getting sums formed by that number.]
6. What patterns do you see on the sheet of possible combinations? (See *Solutions*.)
7. What sum is the most likely according to the theoretical probabilities? [nine]
8. How many of your experimental probabilities were the same as your theoretical probabilities?
9. How can you explain this?

Extensions

1. Create different spinners and have your students logically figure out which would be the most likely sum. (Odd numbers from one to nineteen, even numbers from two to twenty, fractions, etc.)
2. For older students looking for a more challenging mathematical problem, create spinners with sections of different sizes. Have them figure out the probability of landing on each section, and using this information, the most probable sum.

Solutions

The solutions for this problem will vary from group to group because of chance. However, the principle behind the problem remains unchanged. For spinners with the numbers zero to nine, the most likely sum is nine because it is made by the most possible combinations: $0 + 9$, $1 + 8$, $2 + 7$, $3 + 6$, $4 + 5$, $5 + 4$, $6 + 3$, $7 + 2$, $8 + 1$, $9 + 0$.

Following is a chart with all of the possible combinations for the numbers zero to nine. It becomes clear that nine is the most common combination followed by eight and ten, seven and eleven, etc. The sums listed on the bottom and right side of the chart are for the diagonal row which ends in the space above (and to the left of) the sum.

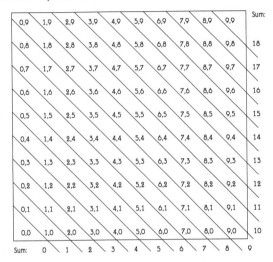

This is the table from the third student sheet with all of the possible combinations filled in.

Sum	Possible Combinations
0	0+0
1	0+1, 1+0
2	0+2, 1+1, 2+0
3	0+3, 1+2, 2+1, 3+0
4	0+4, 1+3, 2+2, 3+1, 4+0
5	0+5, 1+4, 2+3, 3+2, 4+1, 5+0
6	0+6, 1+5, 2+4, 3+3, 4+2, 5+1, 6+0
7	0+7, 1+6, 2+5, 3+4, 4+3, 5+2, 6+1, 7+0
8	0+8, 1+7, 2+6, 3+5, 4+4, 5+3, 6+2, 7+1, 8+0
9	0+9, 1+8, 2+7, 3+6, 4+5, 5+4, 6+3, 7+2, 8+1, 9+0
10	1+9, 2+8, 3+7, 4+6, 5+5, 6+4, 7+3, 8+2, 9+1
11	2+9, 3+8, 4+7, 5+6, 6+5, 7+4, 8+3, 9+2
12	3+9, 4+8, 5+7, 6+6, 7+5, 8+4, 9+3
13	4+9, 5+8, 6+7, 7+6, 8+5, 9+4
14	5+9, 6+8, 7+7, 8+6, 9+5
15	6+9, 7+8, 8+7, 9+6
16	7+9, 8+8, 9+7
17	8+9, 9+8
18	9+9

This table contains many interesting patterns which your students can explore. Following you will find a few described.

1. The number of combinations in the table form a palindrome—they go from one combination to nine combinations and back down again.

2. When written sequentially, as in the example, the numbers farthest right and farthest left are always zero until the sum of 10, at which point the numbers increase from one to nine in a consecutive fashion.

3. If you look at the two sets of diagonals formed—those that go from the middle row up, and those that go from the middle row down—you see that there are two kinds. The first kind is made up of constant numbers, all threes or all nines, for example. The second set is consecutive numbers. These diagonals alternate so that every other diagonal is made up of constant numbers.

This is the table from the fourth student sheet which deals with the theoretical and experimental probability of each sum. The experimental probabilities have been left off because they will be different for each group.

Sum	Total # of Combinations	Theoretical Probability
0	1	P(0)=1/100
1	2	P(1)=2/100
2	3	P(2)=3/100
3	4	P(3)=4/100
4	5	P(4)=5/100
5	6	P(5)=6/100
6	7	P(6)=7/100
7	8	P(7)=8/100
8	9	P(8)=9/100
9	10	P(9)=10/100
10	9	P(10)=9/100
11	8	P(11)=8/100
12	7	P(12)=7/100
13	6	P(13)=6/100
14	5	P(14)=5/100
15	4	P(15)=4/100
16	3	P(16)=3/100
17	2	P(17)=2/100
18	1	P(18)=1/100
Total # of combinations for all sums	100	

Here is how a group's graph might look.

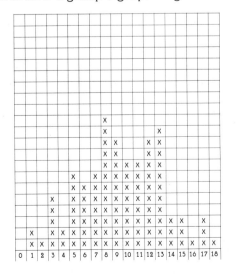

Spinning Sums

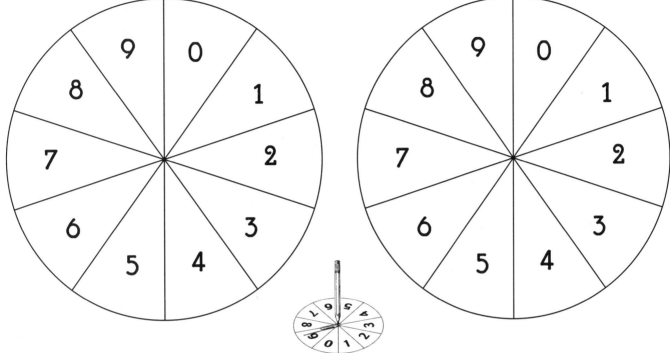

Make each of the numbered circles above into a spinner using a paper clip and a pencil. What are the possible sums if the two spinners are spun?

Which sum do you think is most likely to occur? Why do you think this sum is most likely?

Spin the spinners 100 times. Record each sum by putting an X in the appropriate box on the bar graph on the next page.

Spinning Sums

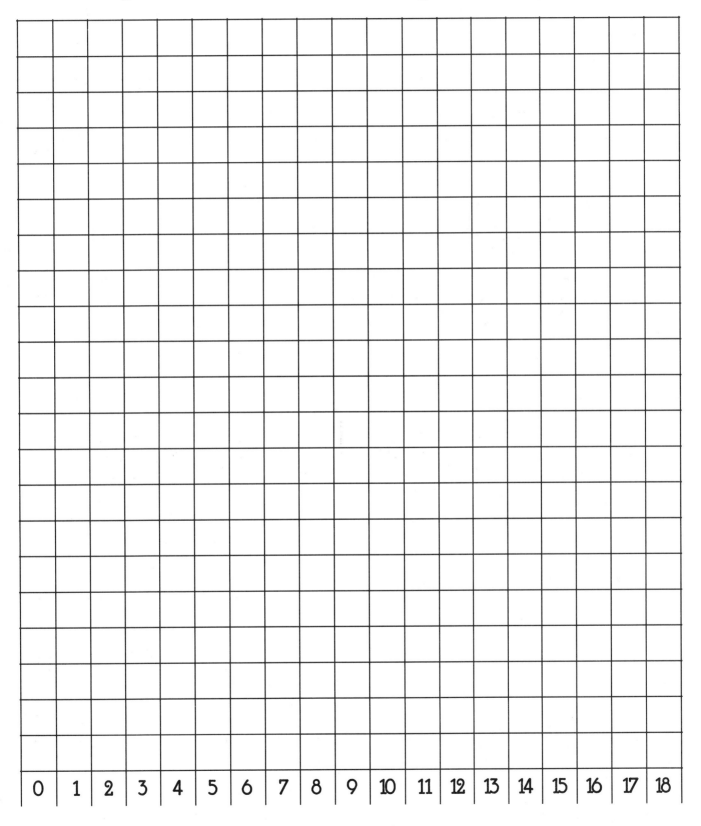

| 0 | 1 | 2 | 3 | 4 | 5 | 6 | 7 | 8 | 9 | 10 | 11 | 12 | 13 | 14 | 15 | 16 | 17 | 18 |

Spinning Sums

4 5 7

Fill in the chart below by writing all of the possible combinations for each sum. For example, to get a one you could either spin a zero and then a one, or a one and then a zero. The first three sums have been done for you.

Sum	Possible Combinations
0	0+0
1	0+1, 1+0
2	0+2, 1+1, 2+0
3	
4	
5	
6	
7	
8	
9	
10	
11	
12	
13	
14	
15	
16	
17	
18	

Spinning Sums

This page deals with theoretical and experimental probability. The table will help you find the theoretical probability of each possible sum from the two zero-to-nine spinners and compare it to the experimental probability that your group got.

The theoretical probability of each sum reflects the number of times that sum is possible in comparison to the total number of combinations possible for all of the sums.

The experimental probability of each sum reflects how many times your group *actually* got that sum in comparison to how many sums you got altogether.

Probabilities are written in a special way. For example, if you wanted to write *"the probability of rolling a sum of two with a pair of dice is one out of 36,"* you would put: *P(2) = 1/36.*

To fill in the theoretical probabilities below you will need to use the information from the third student sheet to find the total number of combinations possible for each sum. Once you have filled in that column, add up all of the numbers to find the total number of combinations possible for all of the sums. Then take the number of ways to get each sum and put it over the total number of combinations possible to get the theoretical probability.

To find the experimental probabilities you will have to use the information from your bar graph that tells how many times your group got each sum. Put that number over the total number of sums that you found to get the experimental probability.

Sum	Total # of Combinations	Theoretical Probability	Experimental Probability
0		P(0) =	P(0) =
1		P(1) =	P(1) =
2		P(2) =	P(2) =
3		P(3) =	P(3) =
4			
5			
6			
7			
8			
9			
10			
11			
12			
13			
14			
15			
16			
17			
18			
Total # of combinations for all sums			

Spinning Sums

When you have completed all of the tables on the previous pages, answer the questions below.

1. Which sum occurred most often in your group?

2. Why do you think this happened?

3. What patterns do you see in the table that lists the possible combinations for each sum?

4. What patterns do you see in the table of theoretical probabilities?

5. Which of your experimental probabilities match up to the theoretical probabilities?

6. Why does this happen?

7. List any other interesting discoveries you made or insights you gained while doing this problem.

The Hundred Number Challenge

Topic
Problem solving, multiple methods of solution

Key Question
How many different ways can you find the sum of the numbers from one to 100?

Focus
Students will find the sum of the numbers from one to 100. However, the focus of the lesson should be on the process of problem solving—not the answer. Students will be challenged to discover multiple methods by which to arrive at the same answer.

Guiding Documents
Project 2061 Benchmarks
- *Mathematics is the study of many kinds of patterns, including numbers and shapes and operations on them. Sometimes patterns are studied because they help to explain how the world works or how to solve practical problems, sometimes because they are interesting in themselves.*
- *Usually there is no one right way to solve a mathematical problem; different methods have different advantages and disadvantages.*

NCTM Standards
- *Use patterns and functions to represent and solve problems*
- *Develop and apply a variety of strategies to solve problems, with emphasis on multistep and nonroutine problems*

Math
Whole number operations
Math patterns

Integrated Processes
Observing
Comparing and contrasting
Generalizing
Applying

Materials
Student sheet
Calculators, optional
Butcher paper, optional

Background Information
There are three things which make this problem especially valuable for students: its historical connection, its emphasis on problem solving, and its potential to be solved in several different ways. To connect your students with the historical elements of the problem, you can read them the following story about Carl Gauss, who was given this problem as a schoolboy.

The Story of Gauss
When the great nineteenth century mathematician Carl Friederich Gauss was an eleven year old student, his teacher, angry with the class for talking, demanded that all of the boys find the sum of the numbers from one to 100. While his classmates began the laborious process of adding all these numbers, Gauss sat thinking. Before his teacher had time to sit back down and get comfortable, Carl wrote the answer on his slate and put it face down on the teacher's desk. Although his teacher was sure that Carl's response was wrong, he waited until everyone had turned in their slates to expose Gauss' hasty foolishness. After some time, when all the slates were collected, he turned them over one by one, each time declaring to the class, "Incorrect." Finally he came to Carl's slate. When he turned it over he discovered, much to his surprise, that Carl Gauss was the only student in the class to have come up with the correct response.

The late George Polya, one of the top mathematicians of the twentieth century, is known for telling his students that it is better to solve one problem five ways than to solve five problems one way. This idea of multiple methods to arrive at the same solution is at the heart of this activity. The method used by Gauss (see *Solutions*) is only one of many which can be used to solve this problem.

Management
1. The goal of this activity is for students to solve the problem in multiple ways. As the teacher, it

is important to facilitate this process. You can do this best by asking leading questions and showing excitement for the problem, not by giving your students the answers.

2. You may or may not want to make calculations available to students as they do this problem.

3. The sharing session is very important, since it allows students to hear multiple methods from their peers. This discussion should broaden all students' problem-solving abilities. Make sure you provide ample time for this important activity.

4. You will need to have a place where students can record their solutions for the class to see. This can be a chalkboard, a bulletin board, or a large sheet of butcher paper.

5. For a more detailed account of the story about Gauss given in the *Background Information*, you may want to use the chapter on Gauss in *Mathematicians are People, Too* (Vol. 1) by Wilbert and Luetta Reimer (1990). The book is available from AIMS.

Procedure

1. Tell the story of Gauss and then hand out the activity sheet, having students work together in groups.

2. Go over the instructions, emphasizing that once a solution has been obtained, the group should attempt to find another way to solve the problem.

3. Once most groups have found multiple ways to reach the solution, come together as a class to share. Have each group fully describe the methods they used to solve the problem.

4. Have students record the various methods on the chalkboard, bulletin board, or a large sheet of paper so that all can see the different solutions as well as hear them.

Discussion

1. What is the sum of the numbers from one to 100? [5050]

2. How did your group first solve the problem?

3. How many different ways did you find to solve the problem?

4. After hearing other groups' methods, can you think of any other ways to get the sum that no one used? Explain.

5. Which method do you think is the easiest for determining the sum?

Extensions

1. Have students use the methods they discovered to add the numbers one to 200, one to 500, or one to 1000.

2. Find the sum of the odd numbers from one to 101.

3. Find the sum of the even numbers from zero to 100.

4. Find the sum of the multiples of five from five to 500.

5. Have students explain why patterns such as those found in solution three below work.

Solutions

This section offers an example of a few of the ways this problem can be approached. This list is by no means exhaustive, and hopefully your students will generate methods that do not appear here.

1. The method attributed to Gauss is to add 1 + 100, 2 + 99, 3 + 98, etc. until you have 50 pairs of 101. You then multiply 50 by 101 to obtain the solution of 5050.

2. A similar method adds 1 + 99, 2 + 98, 3 + 97, etc. giving 49 pairs of 100, with the 100 and the 50 left over. Multiplying 100 by 49 and adding the 150 also gives you 5050.

3. The sum of the numbers 1-10 is 55, the sum of the numbers 11-20 is 155, the sum of the numbers 21-30 is 255, etc. Adding 55 + 155 + 255 + 355 ... + 955 gives you 5050.

4. If you add up all of the digits in the ones place, you will discover that you have 10 sets of 45 (1 + 2 + 3 + 4 + 5 + 6 + 7 + 8 + 9 = 45). If you add up all of the remaining numbers in the tens place, you will have 100 + 200 + 300 ... + 900 (10 x 10 = 100, 10 x 20 = 200, 10 x 30 = 300, etc.). The ten sets of 45 in the ones place give you 450, and the numbers in the tens place give you 4500. Adding this to the 100 that has been left out, you get 5050.

The Hundred Number Challenge

The challenge of this problem is to find the sum of the numbers from one to 100 in at least two different ways. Work with your group to come up with as many different methods of solution as you can. Use the space below and the back of this page to do your work. Be prepared to share your methods with the rest of the class.

1+2+3+....98+99+100

Cutting CORNERS

Topic
Capacity and volume

Key Question
What are all the different-sized square-bottomed boxes that can be made from a sheet of centimeter grid paper?

Focus
Students will construct different-sized square bottomed boxes from 18 cm x 18 cm grids and compare their capacities (the volume each can hold). They will chart and graph this information and draw conclusions from the data.

Guiding Documents
Project 2061 Benchmarks
- *Graphical display of numbers may make it possible to spot patterns that are not otherwise obvious, such as comparative size and trends.*
- *Tables and graphs can show how values of one quantity are related to values of another.*
- *Organize information in simple tables and graphs and identify relationships they reveal.*

NCTM Standards
- *Model situations using oral, written, concrete, pictorial, graphical, and algebraic methods*
- *Represent and solve problems using geometric models*
- *Analyze functional relationships to explain how a change in one quantity results in a change in another*
- *Represent numerical relationships in one and two dimensional graphs*

Math
Measurement
   length
   width
   height
   capacity
Graphing

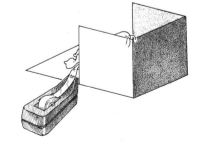

Integrated Processes
Observing
Collecting and recording data
Comparing and contrasting
Identifying and controlling variables
Interpreting data
Generalizing

Materials
Student sheets
Eight copies of the 18 cm x 18 cm grid per group
Tape
Scissors, one pair per student

Background Information
In this activity students construct different-sized boxes from 18 cm x 18 cm grids and compare their capacities (the volume each can hold). To make the boxes, students cut squares from the corners of the grids. With the corners removed, the sides can be folded up and taped to form square-based boxes without tops. If the squares cut out of the corners are limited to whole-number sides, eight boxes can be made. These will range in size from 16 cm x 16 cm x 1 cm to 2 cm x 2 cm x 8 cm. The capacities of the boxes vary and reach a maximum of 432 cubic centimeters with the 12 cm x 12 cm x 3 cm box.

After students have constructed the boxes, they will record data about them in the chart provided and then use these data to make a broken-line graph of their capacities.

A number of different skills and concepts are intertwined in this activity. The concepts of volume and capacity come into play as students build the boxes—this activity provides a good forum to discuss the differences between these two similar, yet different concepts. (Volume is a measure, in cubic units, of the amount of space an object occupies while capacitiy is a measure of the maximum volume a container can hold.) The concepts of maximums and minimums are also present in this activity and may warrant some discussion. The skill of constructing a line graph is incorporated in the activity as students graph their results. The volume formula for a rectangular solid, length times width times height, can be used to find the capacities of the various boxes. As an alternative, students can build a more concrete understanding of volume by counting the number of cubes that would fit in the bottom layer of a box and then multiplying this by the number of layers. This second method may be preferable since it leads to an alternate algorithm— the area of the base times the height—that is more meaningful than the standard algorithm.

Management
1. This activity should be done in groups of four to five.
2. Make sure that you provide each group with enough copies of the grid to make all of the possible boxes,

    © 1999 AIMS Education Foundation

and have some extras on hand in case of mistakes. (With the 18 cm grid provided, the maximum number of boxes is eight.)

3. Be sure to have enough tape and scissors on hand so that the students can all be working simultaneously.

4. Students should be comfortable constructing line graphs before doing this activity.

5. Before groups begin their work, go through the procedure for constructing a box. This should reduce waste from incorrect attempts.

Procedure

1. Distribute the student sheets, scissors, and tape and review the instructions. *Make as many different-sized boxes as you can from several 18 cm x 18 cm grids. Each box should have a square base and no top. Make the boxes by cutting an equal-sized square from each corner of the grid, then folding up the sides and taping the corners.*

2. Have each group make a set of boxes. Then the students in each group can collaborate as they fill in the chart and complete the line graph. (See *Solutions* for graphs.)

3. When each group has finished, close with a time of class discussion where students share their discoveries and any interesting things they noticed about the problem.

Discussion

1. How many boxes were you able to make? [eight]

2. Why couldn't you make more than eight? [With the size grid given, the biggest square you can cut out of the corners is 8 x 8 cm. If you were to cut a 9 x 9 cm square from each corner, you would not be able to make a box.]

3. What discoveries did you make about capacity through this activity?

4. What is the smallest capacity possible? [32 cm³] ...the largest? [432 cm³]

5. What size square should you cut from each corner to yield the largest capacity? [3 x 3 cm]

6. Why does the line graph take the shape that it does? [Once you reach maximum capacity at 432 cm³, the capacity begins to decline quickly.]

7. What does this tell you about boxes that you use in everyday life?

Extensions

1. Use different-sized grids and determine the number of different boxes that can be made and their capacities.

2. Without actually making them, have students graph the boxes which could be created with a grid smaller than 18 x 18, and a grid larger than 18 x 18. Make comparisons between the maximum and minimum capacities of boxes for different-sized grids.

3. Find the smallest possible grid that will make a box.

4. Find the surface area of the exterior of the boxes as well as the difference between surface area and capacity and create a graph. Extension sheets are provided for this activity.

5. For older students, try to find the algebraic formula for calculating the volumes. If graphing calculators are available, use them to graph this function.

Solutions

Below is the table from the student sheet with the correct information inserted. The information for the theoretical boxes zero and nine has been added.

Box Number	Length	Width	Height	Capacity
0	18	18	0	0
1	16	16	1	256
2	14	14	2	392
3	12	12	3	432
4	10	10	4	400
5	8	8	5	320
6	6	6	6	216
7	4	4	7	112
8	2	2	8	32
9	0	0	9	0

Following is how the graph of the capacity of the boxes should look, including the values for box zero and box nine.

Cutting Corners Graph

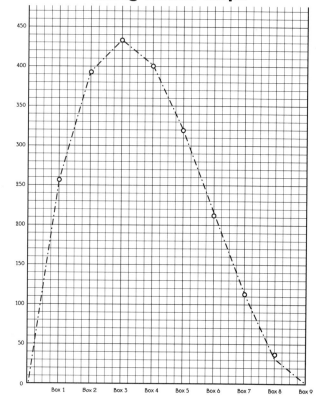

© 1999 AIMS Education Foundation

No matter which method is used to determine capacity, students will discover that the capacities (when starting with the 18 cm grid) reach a maximum when a square with sides of 3 cm is cut out of each corner, and then diminish.

The box with the minimum capacity is the one made by cutting squares with sides of 8 cm out of the corners. It is important to note that this minimum is only the minimum when making boxes according to the instructions. There are two true minimums for this activity which give zero capacities. These occur when no squares (squares with sides of zero) are cut out of the 18 cm grid and when squares with sides of nine are cut out of the grid. Both of these situations preclude boxes from being made. Older students should be encouraged to add these minimum capacities to the graph (when $x = 0$ and $x = 9$).

The formula for finding the capacity of any box from the 18 cm grid is $x(18 - 2x)^2$. In this function, x represents the length of the sides of the squares that are cut from the corners. When the first derivative of this function is found, maximum (at $x = 3$) and minimum (at $x = 9$) values can be determined.

Extension #4

Below is the table from the first extension sheet with the values filled in. Again, the values for the theoretical boxes zero and nine have been included.

Box Number	Capacity	Surface Area	Difference
0	0	324	324
1	256	320	64
2	392	308	84
3	432	288	144
4	400	260	140
5	320	224	96
6	216	180	36
7	112	128	16
8	32	68	36
9	0	0	0

This is how the graph from Extension #4 should look:

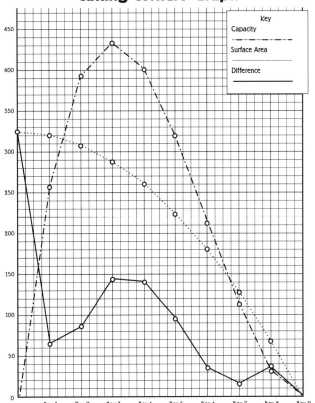

Cutting Corners Graph

Cutting CORNERS

Make as many different-sized boxes as you can using 18 cm x 18 cm grids. Each box should have a square base and no top. Make the boxes by cutting an equal-sized square from each corner of the grid, then folding up the sides and taping the corners.

To make the first box, cut a square with sides of one centimeter from each corner. Label this box number one. For the second box, cut a square with sides of two centimeters from each corner and label it box number two. Squares with three-centimeter sides are cut out for box number three. Continue this process until you have made and labeled all the boxes possible.

Record the dimensions (length, width, and height) of each box. Next, find the capacity of each box (how many cubic centimeters it can hold) and record it.

Cutting CORNERS

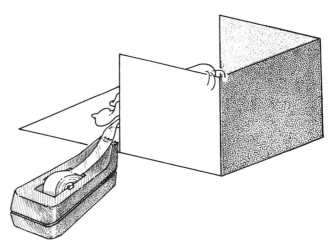

Use this grid to make your boxes.

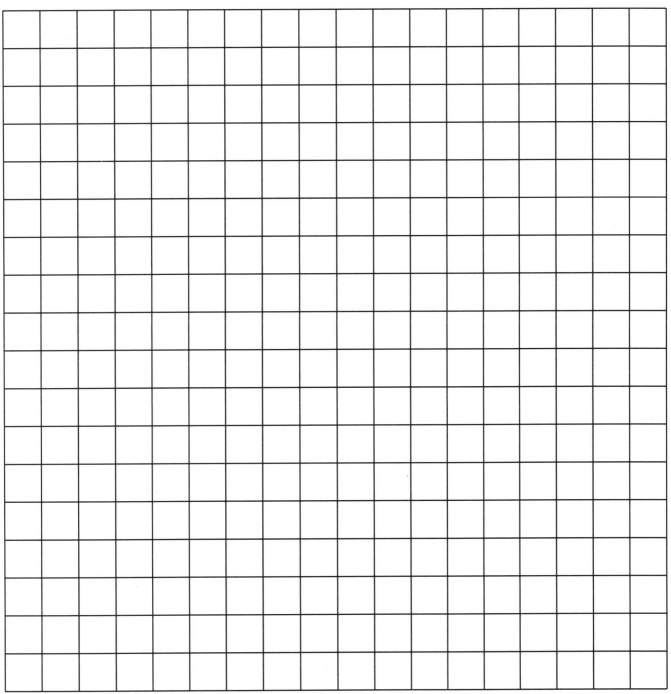

Cutting CORNERS

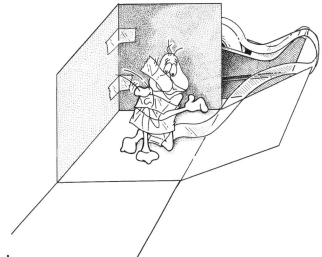

How many boxes did you make?

Fill in this table using the measurements from your boxes.

Box Number	Length	Width	Height	Capacity

What did you discover from the above data?

Use this information to make a broken-line graph on the next page.

Cutting Corners Graph

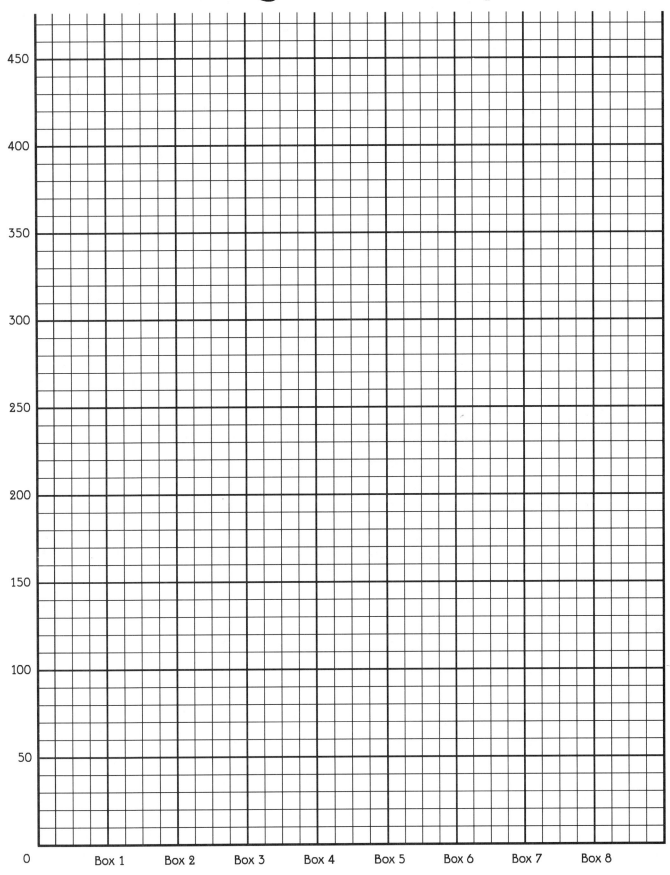

450

400

350

300

250

200

150

100

50

0   Box 1   Box 2   Box 3   Box 4   Box 5   Box 6   Box 7   Box 8

Cutting CORNERS

Now that you have made all of the possible boxes from an 18 x 18 grid, you are going to look at the surface area of each, and compare that to the capacity. To find the surface area of each box, find the area of each face (length x width) and then add all of the areas together.

Complete the table below, using the information from your first table to fill in the capacity values. To find the difference between the capacity and the surface area, subtract the smaller of the two numbers from the larger so that the value is always a positive number.

Box Number	Capacity	Surface Area	Difference

On the next page, graph the capacity, the surface area, and the difference. Use a different-colored pen or pencil for each line and make a key identifying which color represents which measure. After you have made your graph, answer the questions below.

1. What visual patterns do you see when you look at the graph?

2. How can you explain the shapes of the different lines?

Cutting Corners Graph

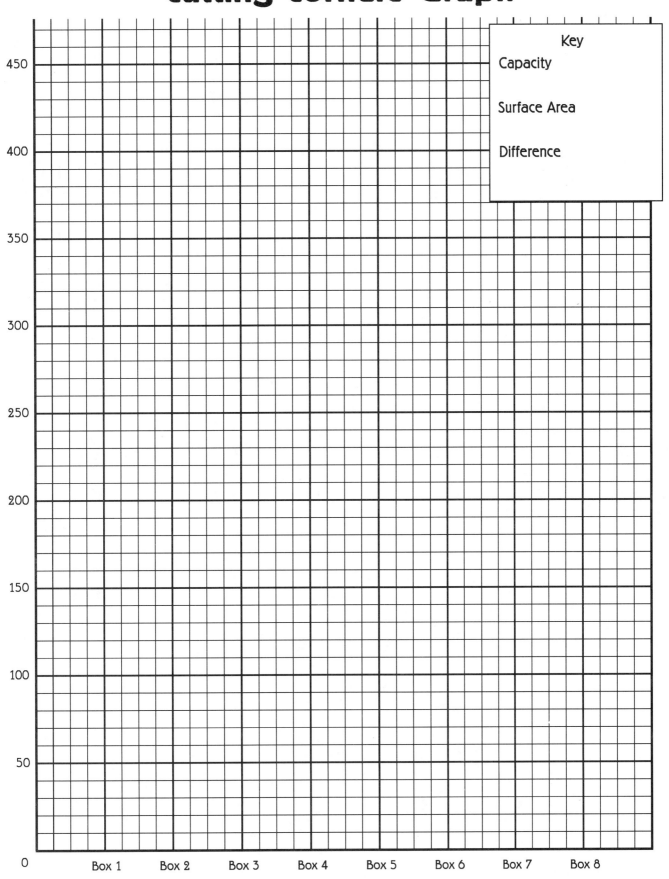

Key

Capacity

Surface Area

Difference

450

400

350

300

250

200

150

100

50

0

Box 1   Box 2   Box 3   Box 4   Box 5   Box 6   Box 7   Box 8

The Fascinating Triangle REVISITED

Topic
Mathematical microworlds

Key Question
How can the numbers one to six be arranged on the sides of a triangle so that the sums of the sides fit one of three criteria:
1. The sums are consecutive numbers?
2. The sums are consecutive even or odd numbers?
3. The sums are other numbers which are equally spaced?

Focus
Students will be challenged to discover patterns that exist in the solutions to this microworld, and then compare these patterns with the patterns they found in *The Fascinating Triangle*.

Guiding Documents
Project 2061 Benchmark
* *Mathematics is the study of many kinds of patterns, including numbers and shapes and operations on them. Sometimes patterns are studied because they help to explain how the world works or how to solve practical problems, sometimes because they are interesting in themselves.*

NCTM Standards
* *Generalize solutions and strategies to new problem situations*
* *Recognize, describe, extend, and create a variety of patterns*

Math
Whole number operations
Math patterns

Integrated Processes
Observing
Comparing and contrasting
Relating
Generalizing
Applying

Materials
Student sheets
Number cards from *The Fascinating Triangle*

Background Information
This investigation started as a simple extension of *The Fascinating Triangle* problem. After exploring this extension however, it soon became evident that it was such a rich mathematical environment that it warranted its own separate, in-depth study. As with *The Fascinating Triangle*, this problem deals with a mathematical microworld which is governed by certain rules that lead to the presence of patterns. These patterns allow students to generalize their solutions and logically explain how these solutions occur. Because this problem has the same structure, but a different rule than *The Fascinating Triangle*, the patterns in the two microworlds can be compared and contrasted, and methods used to solve one can be generalized and applied to the other.

Management
1. In *The Fascinating Triangle Revisited* students will apply techniques and patterns they learned in the previous microworld to solve this new one. They will also be asked to draw comparisons between the two. If it has been a while since you have done *The Fascinating Triangle*, a quick review may be necessary.
2. Have your students use the same number cards they constructed for *The Fascinating Triangle* for this problem.
3. Your role as the teacher is to facilitate students' discovery of patterns and to encourage them to think mathematically about their solutions.

Procedure
1. Distribute the student sheets and go over the directions. *Place the numbers one to six in the six rectangles so that the sums of the three numbers on each side of the triangle fit one of three criteria:*
   a. *The sums are consecutive numbers.*
   b. *The sums are consecutive odd or even numbers.*
   c. *The sums are other numbers that are equally spaced.*
2. Give students time to discover as many different solutions as they can, allowing them to work together or alone.
3. Be sure that students keep an accurate record of their solutions to use in pattern discovery.
4. Have a time of discussion and group sharing where students share the patterns they have discovered as well as any insights they have into the problem.
5. Try to get the students to ask questions that lead to further exploration (see *Discussion*).

Discussion
1. What patterns did you discover in this problem? (See *Solutions*)

2. What do you notice about the corner numbers when a solution is possible? [Various. Their sums are all divisible by three; they are the smallest, even, odd, or largest numbers.]
3. What patterns do you see in the solutions when the smallest numbers are in the corners? ... largest? ... even? ... odd? (See *Solutions*.)
4. What do you notice about different combinations of numbers which give you the same solution? [The sum of the corner numbers is the same.]
5. How are these patterns similar to those you discovered in *The Fascinating Triangle*? [Various. In order to get a solution that fits the criteria, you must have the smallest, even, odd, or largest numbers in the corners; etc.]
6. How are these patterns different? [Various. There are two possible solutions for each of the conditions (small numbers in the corners, etc.) instead of just one; etc.]

Extensions

As with *The Fascinating Triangle*, these extensions should ideally come from the questions raised by the students during the sharing session.
1. Use the numbers two to seven, three to eight, four to nine, etc.
2. Use only odd numbers.
3. Use only even numbers.
4. Use multiples of a number (e.g., 5, 10, 15, 20, 25, 30)

Solutions

These are some of the patterns which your students should discover in this problem. This list is not exhaustive, and hopefully they will discover patterns which are not listed below.
1. The sum of the numbers in the corners is divisible by three when a solution is possible.

$$9 \quad {}_{2}\!\underset{2-5-3}{\overset{6\;\;\nearrow^{1}\!\nwarrow\;4}{}} \quad 8 \qquad 10 \quad {}_{3}\!\underset{3-4-5}{\overset{6\;\;\nearrow^{1}\!\nwarrow\;2}{}} \quad 8$$

10   12

1 + 2 + 3 = **6**   1 + 3 + 5 = **9**

$$12 \quad \underset{5-2-6}{\overset{4 \atop 3 \;\; 1}{}} \quad 11$$

13

4 + 5 + 6 = **15**

2. When using different numbers in the corners that add up to the same total, the same combination of sums will always be possible.

Triangles where the sum of the corners is 12

When the sum of the corners is 12, it is always possible to get the consecutive odd sums of 9, 11, and 13 on the sides.
3. When the smallest numbers are in the corners, two of the criteria that can be met are consecutive sums (8, 9, and 10) and consecutive odd sums (7, 9, and 11).

4. When the even numbers are in the corners, it is not possible to get even sums or consecutive sums. Instead, the two possibilities are: consecutive odd sums (9, 11, and 13) and odd sums with differences of four (7, 11, and 15).

$$9 \quad {}_{4}\!\underset{4-1-6}{\overset{3\;\;\nearrow^{2}\!\nwarrow\;5}{}} \quad 13 \qquad 7 \quad {}_{4}\!\underset{4-5-6}{\overset{1\;\;\nearrow^{2}\!\nwarrow\;3}{}} \quad 11$$

11   15

5. When the odd numbers are in the corners, the two criteria which can be met are: consecutive even sums (8, 10, and 12) and even sums with differences of four (6, 10, and 14).

$$8 \quad {}_{3}\!\underset{3-2-5}{\overset{4\;\;\nearrow^{1}\!\nwarrow\;6}{}} \quad 12 \qquad 6 \quad {}_{3}\!\underset{3-6-5}{\overset{2\;\;\nearrow^{1}\!\nwarrow\;4}{}} \quad 10$$

10   14

6. When the largest numbers are in the corners, it is possible to get consecutive sums (11, 12, and 13) and consecutive even sums (10, 12, and 14).

The Fascinating Triangle REVISITED

In "The Fascinating Triangle," you were asked to place the numbers one to six into a triangle in such a way that the sums on each of the three sides was the same. In this activity, you are challenged to get sums that fit one of the following criteria:

1. The sums are consecutive numbers.
2. The sums are consecutive even or odd numbers.
3. The sums are other numbers that are equally spaced.

Record your solutions on the next page.

The Fascinating Triangle REVISITED

Record your solutions in the spaces below

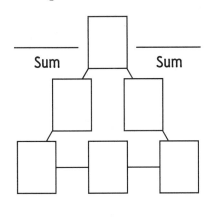

_____ Sum   _____ Sum

_____ Sum

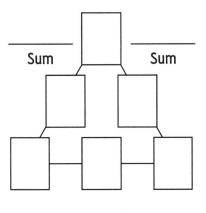

_____ Sum   _____ Sum

_____ Sum

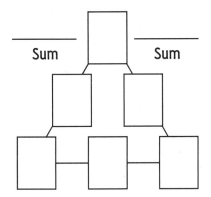

_____ Sum   _____ Sum

_____ Sum

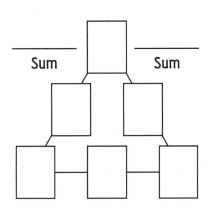

_____ Sum   _____ Sum

_____ Sum

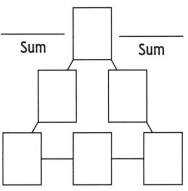

_____ Sum   _____ Sum

_____ Sum

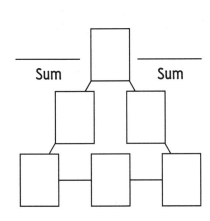

_____ Sum   _____ Sum

_____ Sum

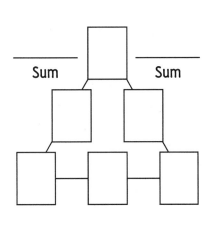

_____ Sum   _____ Sum

_____ Sum

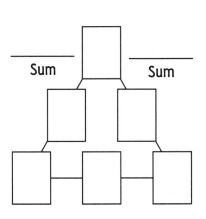

_____ Sum   _____ Sum

_____ Sum

The Fascinating Triangle REVISITED

1. What patterns did you discover in this problem?

2. Which of the patterns are the same as those you found in "The Fascinating Triangle"?

3. Which patterns are different?

4. What other discoveries did you make?

5. Think of some extensions to explore. Report your findings.

THAT'S SUM FACE!

Topic
Mathematical microworlds

Key Question
How can you arrange the numbers one to eight on the vertices of a cube so that the sum of the numbers on each of the six faces is equal?

Focus
Students will study a mathematical microworld, finding solutions and searching for patterns in those solutions.

Guiding Documents
Project 2061 Benchmark
- *Mathematics is the study of many kinds of patterns, including numbers and shapes and operations on them. Sometimes patterns are studied because they help to explain how the world works or how to solve practical problems, sometimes because they are interesting in themselves.*

NCTM Standards
- *Use patterns and relationships to analyze mathematical situations*
- *Recognize, describe, extend and create a variety of patterns*
- *Represent and solve problems using geometric models*

Math
Whole number operations
Geometry and spatial sense
Math patterns

Integrated Processes
Observing
Inferring
Relating
Generalizing

Materials
Method One
    student sheets
    overhead transparency, optional
    drinking straws, six per group
    pipe cleaners, two per group
    paper clips, eight per group
    scissors
    tape

Method Two
    student sheets
    number cards, one through eight,
       three sets per student
    overhead transparencies, optional

Method Three
    student sheets
    overhead transparency
    number cards, one through eight

Background Information
This activity deals with a powerful mathematical microworld. Mathematical microworlds are simple systems with well-defined rules that govern them. While most microworlds seem trivial at first glance, many of them provide an opportunity for sophisticated mathematical exploration. With careful study, some fascinating mathematics can be discovered as students work on this problem.

Management
1. If your students have not worked with mathematical microworlds before, it is strongly recommended that they do so before attempting this activity. *The Fascinating Triangle*, found in this book, can be used as an introduction to microworlds. It is important for students to be familiar with microworlds because this activity involves a three-dimensional figure, the cube. If students are not comfortable solving microworlds that exist on a plane, they will have a hard time making the transition to a three-dimensional problem.
2. Because this activity asks students to visualize and manipulate in the third dimension, several different methods of working on the problem have been designed. Each method approaches the problem in a slightly different way, and requires a different level of spatial-visualization ability. You will need to decide which method(s) is best for your class. You may even want to allow the students to choose which method they prefer, since some are better at spatial visualization than others.

Method One
    The first option is the most concrete and gives students an actual three-dimensional model to help them visualize and manipulate the problem. Each group will need a cube to use as they generate their solutions. The simplest way to make the cubes is to use plastic drinking straws and pipe cleaners

as shown below. It is best to use large pipe cleaners (called chenille strips) because they will not fall out of the straws as easily. Each vertex will require two L-shaped pipe cleaner pieces.

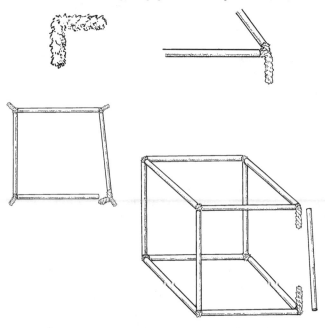

Write the numbers on small pieces of paper. Take paper clips which have been bent as shown, and tape the small pieces of paper to them, creating "flags" which students can put in the different vertices of the cube as they work on the mircoworld.

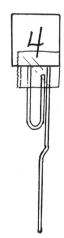

Student sheet one guides students through the cube and number flag construction. The solutions sheet (page three) can be used for students to record their solutions. It may be helpful to make a sample cube for the students to look at as they do their construction.

Method Two

The second option, which uses student sheets two, three, and four, dissects the cube into its individual faces to help students deal with a three-dimensional object in a two-dimensional space.

Students will use the second student sheet to see how the cube is put together, but they will not have to deal with the problem in the third dimension. Page four reduces the cube to six squares, each representing one face of the cube. Students will solve the puzzle on this page, working in the second dimension, then transfer their solutions to the smaller three-dimensional representations on the solutions sheet (page three). For this option, they will need 24 number cards instead of just eight because when put into the second dimension, each of the eight vertices of the cube occurs on three of its faces.

Method Three

The third option, which uses student sheets two and three, is the most abstract, and requires students to be able to visualize a three-dimensional cube from a two-dimensional drawing. They are given a large version of the cube to use while looking for solutions, and a page with several small cubes to record the solutions they discover. This type of problem is much easier for students if they have numbers to move around. Number cards can be made from scratch paper, light cardboard, plastic chips, and many other things. Students will need eight cards each, with the numbers one to eight written on them. You will need to make a transparency of the second student sheet to use when introducing the activity.

For all methods

Student pages five, six, and seven are the follow-up pages for this activity that have students examine the process they have just gone through. Pages five and six are designed to provide students with a structured exploration of the patterns and mathematics inherent in this microworld. The questions do not cover all of the mathematics, but they do enough to show students how much more there is to the problem than just finding the sums. Page seven is designed for those students who are comfortable with an open-ended approach and don't need questions to guide their explorations. Again, you will need to decide which sheets are most appropriate for your class.

3. For this activity students should work in small groups and be encouraged to collaborate. As soon as one person finds a solution, it should be shared with the other members of the group. Students need to have multiple solutions before they can begin to see the patterns and mathematics involved in this microworld.

Procedure
Method One

1. Give a brief review of microworlds, perhaps using an activity such as *The Fascinating Triangle* to refresh students' memories.

2. Introduce this problem by going over the rules for the microworld. You may want to use an overhead transparency of student sheet two for this, but explain to students that they will be building a model of the cube instead of doing the problem on paper. *Place the numbers one to eight at the vertices of the cube so that the sum of the numbers on each face is the same.*

3. Have students get into their groups and hand out student sheet one and the materials needed to construct the cube.

4. Go over the directions for cube construction and allow groups time to complete their cube and number the flags.

5. Once groups have successfully built their cubes, hand out student sheet three and have them begin to search for solutions.

6. When each group has recorded several solutions, distribute student sheet five and six or seven and give students ample time to recognize the many patterns present in the microworld.

7. Close with a class discussion time where students share their solutions as well as any patterns and interesting discoveries they made while solving the problem.

Method Two

1. Give a brief review of microworlds, perhaps using an activity such as *The Fascinating Triangle* to refresh students' memories.

2. Introduce the problem by handing out student sheet two and going over the rules for the microworld. You may find it helpful to make overhead transparencies of student sheets two and four to use during your explanation. *Place the numbers one to eight at the vertices of the cube so that the sum of the numbers on each face is the same.*

3. Hand out student sheets two, three, and four and make sure students understand how the transition has been made from three to two dimensions using the six squares to represent the cube's faces. Be sure to explain to your students that their challenge as stated on the fourth page is the same as the one stated on the second page, they are just going about it in a different way.

4. Have students make their number cards, creating three cards for each number from one to eight.

5. While working in small groups, direct the students to find as many solutions as possible.

6. When each group has recorded several solutions, distribute student sheet five and six or seven and give students ample time to recognize the many patterns present in the microworld.

7. Close with a class discussion time where students share their solutions as well as any patterns and interesting discoveries they made while solving the problem.

Method Three

1. Give a brief review of microworlds, perhaps using an activity such as *The Fascinating Triangle* to refresh students' memories.

2. Explain the rules of this microworld using the overhead transparency of student sheet two. *Place the numbers one to eight at the vertices of the cube so that the sum of the numbers on each face is the same.*

3. Help students visualize the six faces in this two-dimensional representation of the cube. Make sure everyone understands the problem before distributing student sheets two and three.

4. Have students create their number cards, using paper, cardboard, plastic chips, or whatever is available.

5. While working in small groups, direct the students to find as many solutions as possible.

6. When each group has recorded several solutions, distribute student sheets five and six or seven and give students ample time to recognize the many patterns present in the microworld.

7. Close with a class discussion time where students share their solutions as well as any patterns and interesting discoveries they made while solving the problem.

Discussion

1. What sums did you discover for the faces of the cube? [Eighteen is the only possible sum.]

2. Why is 18 the only possible sum? (See *Solutions*.)

3. How many solutions did you discover?

4. How many of these solutions are unique (i.e., not mirror images or rotations)? [There are only three unique solutions.]

5. What patterns did you discover in your solutions? (See *Solutions*.)

Extensions

1. Use numbers other than one to eight such as two to nine, three to 10, etc. and compare the patterns in the solutions, trying to make some generalizations.

2. Use consecutive odd or even numbers (2, 4, 6, etc.).

3. Find all of the rotations and mirror images for each of the solutions.

4. Have students create informal proofs for why there are only three unique solutions possible for any given set of numbers.

Solutions

What follows are the solutions to the problem, as well as an in-depth look at the reasons behind the solutions. There is also a discussion of some of the patterns which are apparent in the solutions. Although you will probably be unable to use all of this information with your class, hopefully it will help give you a deeper understanding of the problem and enable you to guide your students to some fascinating discoveries. If you have not yet done the problem yourself, you are strongly encouraged to do so. These solutions were written with the expectation that the reader has attempted to solve the problem.

There are only three unique solutions for the numbers one to eight. All other solutions are rotations or mirror images of the ones presented below.

You will notice that the faces on each cube have a sum of 18—the only sum possible using the numbers one to eight. This has to do with the sum of the numbers being used. The sum of the numbers one to eight is 36. Since the numbers are placed on the vertices of the cube, and each vertex touches three faces, each number is used three times. For example, the number eight would be added three different times—once for each face of which it is a part. Because of this, the value of the number eight is actually 24. Likewise, the value of the number seven is 21, the value of the number six is 18, and so on. Therefore, the total value of the eight vertices is 3 x 36 (the sum of one to eight), or 108. If you divide 108 by six (the number of faces) you are left with 18—the sum for each face. This principle can be used for any set of numbers to discover the sum of each face. For example, with the even numbers two to 16, the sum of each face is 36. [2 + 4 + 6 + 8 + 10 + 12 + 14 + 16 = 72; 72 x 3 = 216; 216/6 = 36].

In-Depth

The reason that there are only three unique solutions for a given set of eight numbers has to do with the antipodes. The antipodes are the numbers at opposite corners of the cube, as illustrated below.

	Antipodal points
F—G A+B E+H C—D	A-H B-E C-G D-F

As you can see in the diagram, there are four antipodal points for any given cube. When we look at the solutions for the numbers one to eight, we see that there are three possible differences between the antipodes, giving three unique solutions. It is possible to have a difference of one, two, and four between the antipodal points. Differences of three, five, and six are not possible. There are a couple of reasons for this. To understand the first reason, it is necessary to look at all of the possible four-number combinations which will yield a sum of 18. These combinations can be thought of as representing the potential faces of a given cube.

Combinations

1. 8, 7, 2, 1   5. 7, 6, 4, 1
2. 8, 6, 3, 1   6. 7, 6, 3, 2
3. 8, 5, 4, 1   7. 7, 5, 4, 2
4. 8, 5, 3, 2   8. 6, 5, 4, 3

Notice that there are eight possible combinations that have a sum of 18 in which each number from one to eight is used a total of four times. However, there are only six faces on a cube, so any one solution will leave two of these potential combinations unused. The rules of this microworld state that one number is placed at each of the eight vertices of the cube. This means that each number from one to eight is counted three times, since each vertex is a part of three faces. Therefore, all valid solutions will always contain six of the eight combinations which use each number a total three times between them. It follows then, that the two unused combinations will always consist of all the numbers from one to eight because each number will have already been used three times in the solution.

For example, it is impossible to have a solution consisting of the combinations three through eight above because that leaves out combinations one and two. Combinations one and two contain the numbers eight, seven, two, one, eight, six, three, and one. As you can see, the numbers eight and one occur in both of them, and the numbers four and five do not occur at all. This would indicate that the numbers four and five were used four times in the solution, and the numbers eight and one were used only twice, which, as we have already established, is not possible.

Now we must return to the antipodes. To have a difference of one between the antipodal points, eight must be opposite from seven, six must be opposite from five, four must be opposite from three, and two must be opposite from one. In order for that to happen, those numbers cannot occur together in any of the combinations which are used. If they occur together in a combination, this indicates that they are on the same face of the cube, making it impossible for them to be

antipodes. What we discover therefore, is that for each possible difference the two unused combinations will each contain two antipodal pairs. You can see that this is true by looking at the solutions below.

Difference of 4 **Difference of 2** **Difference of 1**

Missing combinations

8, 5, 4, 1	8, 6, 3, 1	8, 7, 2, 1
7, 6, 3, 2	7, 5, 4, 2	6, 5, 4, 3

Notice above that for a difference of four, the unused combinations contain eight and four and five and one together; and seven and three and six and two together. In the cube, you can see that these numbers form the antipodal points. This is also true for differences of two and one.

When attempting to have an antipodal difference of three, five, or six, you quickly discover that it is not possible. To have a difference of three you would have to have eight opposite five, seven opposite four, six opposite three, five opposite two, and four opposite one. The obvious problem is that the numbers five and four were used twice—an impossibility when dealing with this microworld. The same problem occurs with five and six because one cannot create possible pairings of numbers which give those differences using the numbers one to eight.

All of this demonstrates that there are only three unique solutions possible for any set of eight numbers within this microworld.

Patterns

When looking at the solutions to the problem, there are several patterns which present themselves. This listing is certainly not complete, there are many things that your students may discover which are not written here.

1. As already mentioned, the differences between the opposite corners of the cube (antipodes) are constant within that cube. Possible differences for the numbers one to eight are one, two, and four.

7 - 3 = 4	4 - 2 = 2	8 - 7 = 1
8 - 4 = 4	7 - 5 = 2	4 - 3 = 1
5 - 1 = 4	3 - 1 = 2	6 - 5 = 1
6 - 2 = 4	8 - 6 = 2	2 - 1 = 1

2. Antipodal (opposite) edges of the cube have the same sum, but the sum is not constant throughout the cube.

6 + 4 = 10, 8 + 2 = 10
1 + 7 = 8, 3 + 5 = 8
1 + 6 = 7, 2 + 5 = 7
7 + 4 = 11, 8 + 3 = 11

3. Each face has two odd and two even numbers.

4. In each cube, there are three sets of parallel edges, the "length" and the "width" and the "height." When looking at the sums of these edges, some interesting patterns come to light.

	"Height"	"Width"	"Length"
	4 + 5 = 9	7 + 4 = 11	1 + 7 = 8
	6 + 3 = 9	1 + 6 = 7	6 + 4 = 10
	1 + 8 = 9	8 + 3 = 11	3 + 5 = 8
	7 + 2 = 9	2 + 5 = 7	8 + 2 = 10
	1 + 7 = 8	8 + 1 = 9	5 + 8 = 13
	4 + 6 = 10	5 + 4 = 9	4 + 1 = 5
	5 + 3 = 8	3 + 6 = 9	6 + 7 = 13
	8 + 2 = 10	2 + 7 = 9	3 + 2 = 5
	1 + 4 = 5	8 + 1 = 9	3 + 8 = 11
	6 + 7 = 13	3 + 6 = 9	6 + 1 = 7
	3 + 2 = 5	2 + 7 = 9	7 + 4 = 11
	8 + 5 = 13	5 + 4 = 9	2 + 5 = 7

Notice that in every cube, one set of parallel edges always has a sum of nine. The total sum of each set of parallel edges is 36—twice 18.

THAT'S SUM FACE!

What you need:

Six plastic drinking straws
Two pipe cleaners
Scissors
Eight paper clips

Paper
Pen or pencil
Tape

Step One
Cut the drinking straws in half so that you have 12 pieces that are the same length.

Step Two
Cut each of the pipe cleaners into eighths and use the pieces to make joints as shown.

Step Three
Each vertex requires two L-shaped joints. Fit each joint with three straws and attach them all to form a cube.

 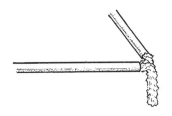 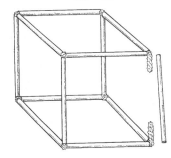

Step Four
Cut out eight small pieces of paper and number them from one to eight. Take the paper clips and straighten one end, as shown. Tape the numbers to the top of the paper clips to create number flags.

The Challenge
Now that you have your cube and your numbers, your challenge is to place the numbers at the vertices of the cube so that the sum of the numbers on each face is the same. You can move your flags around by placing the paper clips into the straws at the vertices. When you find a solution, make a record of it.

THAT'S SUM FACE!

The drawing below represents a cube. Can you "see" the six faces in this drawing?

The challenge is to place the numbers one to eight in the circles below so that the sum of the numbers on each face is the same. When you have a solution, record it on the next page. The letters by the vertices will help you describe your solutions when you share with the class.

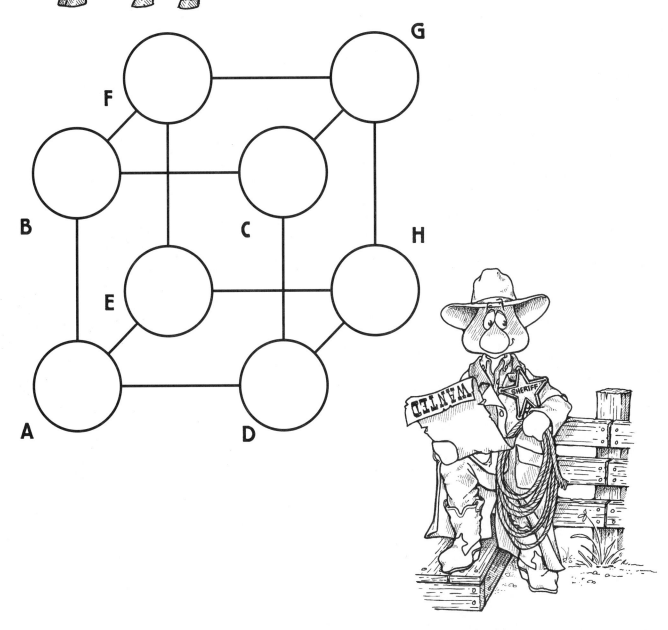

THAT'S SUM FACE!

Use this page to record your solutions, being sure to match the correct number to the space which has the corresponding letter.

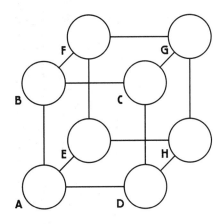
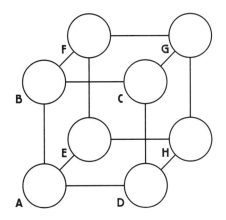
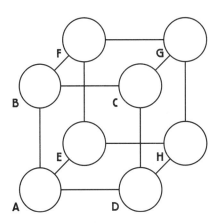

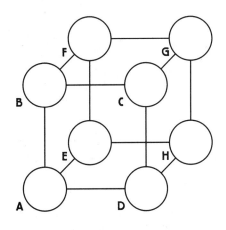
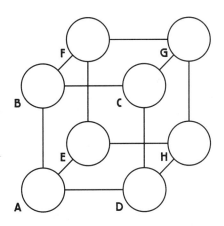
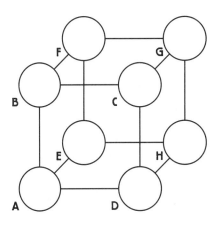

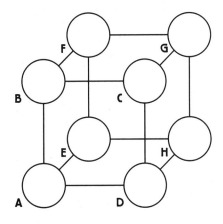
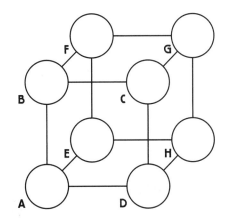
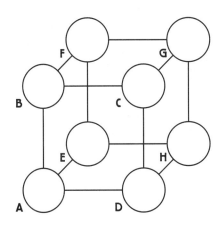

THAT'S SUM FACE!

This page shows a cube broken down into its six faces. Each face is labeled by the letters at the vertices and by its position on the cube. Your challenge is to put the numbers one to eight into the spaces below so that the sum of each square is the same. Because the squares represent the faces of a cube, each number may be used three times. Whenever a given number is placed into a circle with a certain letter, that same number must go into the other two spaces with that letter. All spaces which are the same letter represent a single vertex of the cube, so when you record a solution, each number will only be used once. As you find solutions, record them on the solutions sheet.

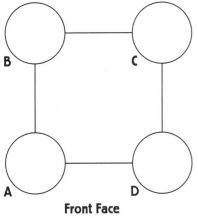

Left Face

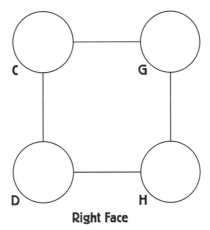

Top Face

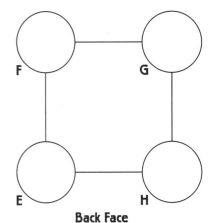

Right Face

Back Face

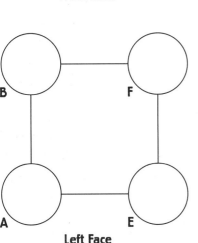

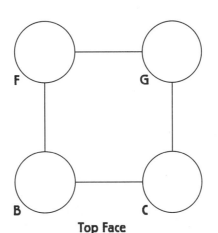

Bottom Face

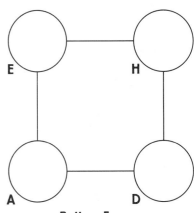

THAT'S SUM FACE!

Bob Wirtz, a famous mathematics educator, once said, "You've got the answer, now the mathematics begins." There is a world of mathematics to be discovered in the cube activity you've been doing. Use the questions below to help you find some of the mathematics hidden in this microworld.

What type of strategy did you use to find answers to this problem? If you used trial-and-error, try to come up with a more systematic way of finding solutions. Describe this new approach.

What is the sum on each of the six faces? Why is this the sum?
Describe how this sum is related to the numbers 1-8.

What do you notice about the placement of the 1 and 8 in each solution?

Why does this happen?

THAT'S SUM FACE!

Look at the sums on parallel edges of the cube. What do you notice?

What do you notice about odd and even numbers in this problem?

Look at the numbers at opposite corners of the cube (mathematicians call these antipodal points). What do you notice?

Try to find some other patterns in your answers and list them below.

What extensions to this problem can you think of to explore?

THAT'S SUM FACE!

Bob Wirtz, a famous mathematics educator, once said, "You've got the answer, now the mathematics begins." There is a world of mathematics to be discovered in the cube activity you've been doing. Your task is to study the answers on the solutions sheet and use these answers to help you explore this microworld in depth. This exploration should help you discover some of the mathematics hidden therein. Use the space below and on the back of this sheet to record your discoveries.

Topic
Patterns

Key Question
What mathematical patterns can you discover in this puzzle?

Focus
Students will learn how to solve the puzzle, then work to find the mathematical patterns which exist in the solutions.

Guiding Documents
Project 2061 Benchmark
* *Mathematics is the study of many kinds of patterns, including numbers and shapes and operations on them. Sometimes patterns are studied because they help to explain how the world works or how to solve practical problems, sometimes because they are interesting in themselves.*

NCTM Standards
* *Describe, extend, analyze, and create a wide variety of patterns*
* *Relate physical materials, pictures, and diagrams to mathematical ideas*
* *Represent situations and number patterns with tables, graphs, verbal rules, and equations*

Math
Math patterns
Algebraic thinking

Integrated Processes
Observing
Comparing and contrasting
Generalizing
Applying

Materials
Student sheets
Eight markers per student, four of one color, four of another (see *Management 3*)
Overhead transparency of puzzle and translucent colored objects, optional

Background Information
Slides and Jumps is an adaptation of a difficult peg puzzle that has been around for many years and appears, at first glance, to have no mathematical content. However, by simplifying it becomes easier to solve, and the richness of its mathematical patterns and possibilities is revealed. Having students solve multiple levels of the puzzle allows them to start easy, thereby easing frustration, and see the patterns that develop through the different levels.

The object of the puzzle is to have the markers of different colors exchange places by following certain rules. Markers can move by sliding into an empty space, or by jumping over a single marker (of either color) into an empty space. Markers can only move in one direction—no going backwards.

As students solve this puzzle using the official rules, they will discover three "unwritten rules" which will help them solve it more consistently. The first of these is that whenever you get two markers of the same color next to each other in the middle of the board after a move, you will be blocked and have to start over. The second rule is that you must move the marker out of the end space when the space next to it opens up. The final unwritten rule is that you must move as many markers of one color as you can without breaking the rules, then switch to the other color and do the same thing. This process must be repeated until you have switched all of the markers. Once these unwritten rules are discovered, students will find it easier to solve each level, allowing them to focus their efforts on the patterns and not the mechanics of the solutions.

Management
1. This problem has been divided into two parts. In *Part 1*, students will solve the puzzle, and in *Part 2*, they will look for the patterns which exist in the solutions. *Part 2* has been designed to provide you with a choice of a structured or an open-ended approach. Choose the format best suited to your class, and give them the corresponding student sheet. The second student sheet is the structured sheet, and the third student sheet is the unstructured sheet.
2. It is important to give enough time to each part of this problem for it to be successful. Students must be good at solving the puzzle before they can see the variety of patterns that it produces, and this takes time! Because of this, you may want to do *Part 1* on one day and *Part 2* on another. This way students have had lots of time to master the puzzle before they begin to search for patterns.
3. Each student will need eight markers to do this problem, four of one color, and four of another. Items such as Friendly Bears, Flying Astronauts, Math Chips, or pennies and nickels will all work well, as long as there are two distinct colors and/or types.

4. When students are working on *Part 1*, make sure that they come to a point where they can solve each level of the puzzle every time without making a mistake. If your students are having a hard time discovering the unwritten rules which will allow them to do this, help them by having them verbalize their moves and explain what they are doing at each step. This should not be a competitive time in which students try to outdo each other by solving a level faster, but a collaborative time in which students work together to understand the process.

5. During *Part 2*, have students work in pairs to come up with as many patterns as they can. Now that the mechanics of the puzzle have been mastered, the focus should be on exploring the many interesting patterns which exist. The most effective way to do this is to have one student solve the puzzle at each level, while the other student records. It helps if the student solving the puzzle verbalizes the moves they are making. For example, the solution to the first level could be verbalized: "Green slides left, red jumps right, green slides left." It is by looking at the solutions when they have been recorded in a variety of different ways that most of the patterns will be discovered.

Procedure

Part 1

1. Hand out the student sheet for *Part 1* and eight markers (four each of two colors) to each student. Explain the directions, using the overhead to demonstrate if necessary. *At each level of the puzzle, place an equal number of markers at each end of the row, leaving one empty space in the middle. For example, in Level 1, you might place one red marker in the left space and a green one in the right. The object of the puzzle is to have the two colors of markers exchange places. The markers on the right can move to the left by sliding into an adjacent empty space or by jumping over one marker (of either color) into an empty space. The markers on the left move in the same fashion, but in the opposite direction. Each color of marker can move in one direction only—markers cannot go backwards. Write the color of the markers you are putting on each side over the appropriate arrow.*

2. Have students solve the four levels of the puzzle presented. Do not move on to *Part 2* until *all* students can solve up to *Level 4* every time without making a mistake. Encourage students to help each other solve the puzzle. Those who are not completely proficient at the solving process will be unable to discover the rich patterns that exist in this puzzle in the second part of the activity.

3. Have a class discussion using the discussion questions for *Part 1* to help the class verbalize and understand the unwritten rules which govern the game.

Part 2

1. Hand out either the second or third student sheet and make sure the class understands that there are *many* patterns to be discovered.

2. Have students get in pairs and record their solutions, leaving sufficient time for them to make discoveries and explore the patterns that exist.

3. Come together for a time of discussion and exploration where students share the patterns they discovered. If some of the more obvious or interesting patterns have been overlooked, lead the class in a time of group discovery (see *Solutions*).

Discussion

Part 1

1. Are there any "unwritten rules" that help you solve the puzzle? [Yes]

2. What are they? [(a) If you make a move that places two markers of the same color next to each other in the middle, you will be stuck. (b) You must move the marker out of the end space when the space next to it opens up. (c) Move as many markers of one color as you can without breaking the rules, then switch to the other color and do the same thing. Repeat this process until you have switched all of the markers.]

3. How did you discover these rules? [Various. Trial and error, thought about the process, etc.]

Part 2

1. What patterns did you see emerging in the solutions for the different levels? (See *Solutions.*)

2. Which of these patterns are related to the markers? ... the boxes? ... the moves? (See *Solutions.*)

Extensions

1. Have older students find the *n*th term for the number of boxes (3, 5, 7, 9, etc.) [2*n* + 1].

2. Find the *n*th term for the number of markers (2, 4, 6, 8, etc.) [2*n*].

3. Start with an uneven number of markers on each side. For example, on *Level 4*, start with three markers on one side and five markers on the other instead of four and four. Then try two and six, one and seven, and finally zero and eight.

4. Use an even number of squares on each level instead of an odd number. (*Level 1*, four squares; *Level 2*, six squares; etc.)

5. Solve the problem without the restriction of only being able to move markers forwards.

Solutions

The first two pages of the solutions are step-by-step illustrations for the solutions of each level from one to four. Following this section is a discussion of a few of the many patterns which exist in the problem. Hopefully your students will discover some which are not mentioned.

These solutions show how to solve each level in the fewest possible moves. Each level can begin with either the red or the green chip making the first move. In these solutions, the color which moves first has been switched with every level.

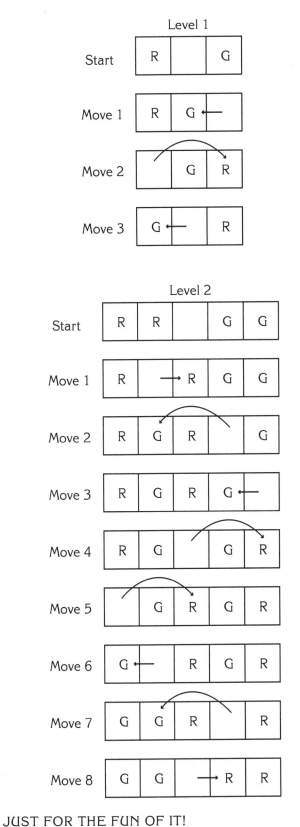

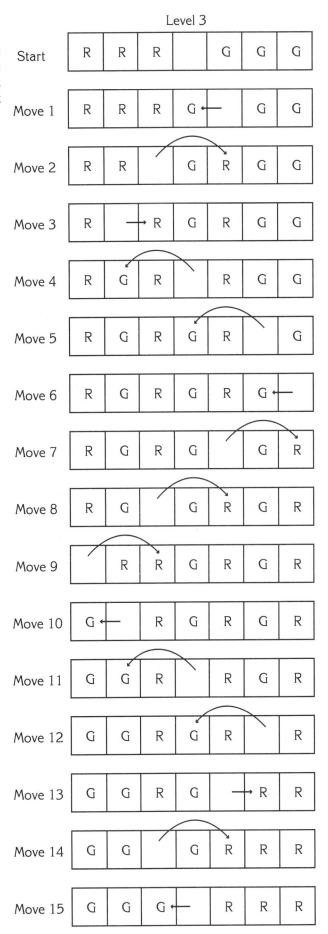

Level 4

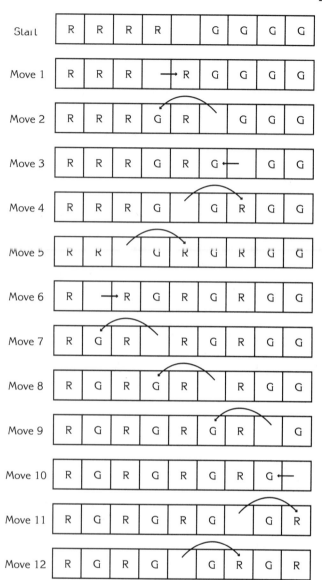

Start | R R R R _ G G G G

Move 1 | R R R → R G G G G

Move 2 | R R R G R _ G G G

Move 3 | R R R G R G ← _ G G

Move 4 | R R R G _ G R G G

Move 5 | R R _ G R G R G G

Move 6 | R → R G R G R G G

Move 7 | R G R _ R G R G G

Move 8 | R G R G R _ R G G

Move 9 | R G R G R G R _ G

Move 10 | R G R G R G R G ←

Move 11 | R G R G R G _ G R

Move 12 | R G R G _ G R G R

Move 13 | R G _ G R G R G R

Move 14 | _ G R G R G R G R

Move 15 | G ← _ R G R G R G R

Move 16 | G G R _ R G R G R

Move 17 | G G R G R _ R G R

Move 18 | G G R G R G R _ R

Move 19 | G G R G R G _ R R

Move 20 | G G R G _ G R R R

Move 21 | G G _ G R G R R R

Move 22 | G G G ← _ R G R R R

Move 23 | G G G G R _ R R R

Move 24 | G G G G → R R R R

---

1. *Level 1* take three moves, *Level 2* takes eight moves, *Level 3* takes 15 moves, *Level 4* takes 24 moves, and so on. The difference between three and eight is five; between eight and 15 is seven; between 15 and 24 is nine; and so on. The differences keep going up by consecutive odd numbers. Thus, if there were a *Level 5* it would require 35 moves (the difference between 24 and 35 is 11—the next odd number).

Level	Moves	Difference
1	3	
2	8	5
3	15	7
4	24	9
5	35	11
n	$n^2 + 2n$	$2n + 1$

2. The numbers of moves for each level are the square numbers (starting with four) minus one.

Level	Moves
1	$3 = (2^2 - 1)$
2	$8 = (3^2 - 1)$
3	$15 = (4^2 - 1)$
4	$24 = (5^2 - 1)$
5	$35 = (6^2 - 1)$
n	$(n + 1)^2 - 1$

3. The number of boxes is always one more than the number of markers.

Markers		Boxes
2	(+ 1)	3
4	(+ 1)	5
6	(+ 1)	7
8	(+ 1)	9
n		$n+1$

4. The number of markers is twice the number of the level you are on.

Level		Markers
1	(x 2)	2
2	(x 2)	4
3	(x 2)	6
4	(x 2)	8
n		$2n$

5. The number of boxes for each level is the consecutive odd numbers (beginning with three). *Level 1*: three boxes, *Level 2*: five boxes, *Level 3*: seven boxes, *Level 4*: nine boxes, etc.

Level	Boxes
1	3
2	5
3	7
4	9
n	$2n + 1$

6. The number of jumps per level is the number of the level squared.

Level	Jumps
1	1 (1^2)
2	4 (2^2)
3	9 (3^2)
4	16 (4^2)
n	n^2

7. The number of slides per level is the number of the level times two.

Level		Slides
1	(x 2)	2
2	(x 2)	4
3	(x 2)	6
4	(x 2)	8
n		$2n$

8. The number of markers of each color is equivalent to the level you are on.

9. When looking at the direction of the moves (to the left and right), the following pattern emerges:

Level 1: three moves: 1l ,1r ,1l
Level 2: eight moves: 1l, 2r, 2l, 2r, 1l
Level 3: fifteen moves: 1l, 2r, 3l, 3r, 3l, 2r, 1l
Level 4: twenty four moves:
 1r, 2l, 3r, 4l, 4r, 4l, 3r, 2l, 1r

Translating these moves into numbers also reveals some interesting patterns:

Level 1:   111
Level 2:   12221
Level 3: 1233321
Level 4: 123444321

10. When arranging the slides (S) and jumps (J) made at each level by starting a new line whenever the color moved changes, the following patterns emerge:

Level 1	Level 2	Level 3	Level 4
S	S	S	S
J	JS	JS	JS
S	JJ	JJS	JJS
	SJ	JJJ	JJJS
	S	SJJ	JJJJ
		SJ	SJJJ
		S	SJJ
			SJ
			S

When viewing the slides and jumps in a linear fashion, the pattern looks like this:

SJS
SJSJJSJS
SJSJJSJJJSJJSJS
SJSJJSJJJSJJJJSJJJSJJSJS

Notice that each line is a palindrome, it is the same whether you read it from left to right or right to left.

11. The solutions can also be put into a matrix, revealing some more interesting patterns. To create a matrix, each set of unique "resting positions" that the pieces take during a given solution is recorded in order, omitting the empty space. The rows in the matrix are NOT a record of every move for each level, they are a record of the unique positions that the pieces are in between moves, the resting positions. Because the empty space is omitted, there are several resting positions that are the same. In these matrices, all duplicate positions have been eliminated, accounting for the difference between the number of rows in the matrix and the actual number of resting positions for each level.

For example, the matrix for *Level 2* has only five rows, although there are nine total resting positions for this level. If we first look at the resting positions of the pieces and compare these to the rows in the matrix, it becomes clear that four of the positions are omitted from the matrix because they are repetitive. In this case, + and o have been used to distinguish the colors.

Resting positions	Matrix rows
1. ++__oo	++oo
2. ++o__o	
3. +__o+o	+o+o
4. __+o+o	
5. o+__+o	o++o
6. o+o+__	o+o+
7. o+o__+	
8. o__o++	oo++
9. oo__++	

Without the space (__), resting positions one and two are the same, positions three and four are the same, positions six and seven are the same, and positions eight and nine are the same.

This same method was used to determine all of the rows which appear in the matrices below.

$$
\begin{array}{c|c}
o & + \\
\hline
+ & o
\end{array}
$$

Level 1

$$
\begin{array}{c|c}
++ & oo \\
+o & +o \\
o+ & +o \\
o+ & o+ \\
oo & ++
\end{array}
$$

Level 2

$$
\begin{array}{c|c}
ooo & +++ \\
oo+ & o++ \\
oo+ & +o+ \\
o+o & +o+ \\
+oo & +o+ \\
+o+ & oo+ \\
+o+ & o+o \\
+o+ & +oo \\
++o & +oo \\
+++ & ooo
\end{array}
$$

Level 3

$$
\begin{array}{c|c}
++++ & oooo \\
+++o & +ooo \\
+++o & o+oo \\
++o+ & o+oo \\
+o++ & o+oo \\
+o+o & ++oo \\
+o+o & +o+o \\
+o+o & +oo+ \\
+o+o & o+o+ \\
+oo+ & o+o+ \\
o+o+ & o+o+ \\
oo++ & o+o+ \\
oo+o & ++o+ \\
oo+o & +o++ \\
oo+o & o+++ \\
ooo+ & o+++ \\
oooo & ++++
\end{array}
$$

Level 4

When examining the matrices, several patterns begin to emerge.

a. The number of unique positions that the pieces take during a level depends on the number of pieces which begin for that level. The levels which use an even number of pieces (one and three) have an even number of unique positions (two and ten, respectively). The levels which use an odd number of pieces (two and four) have an odd number of unique positions (five and 17, respectively).

b. The number of rows in a matrix is the number of the level squared, plus one.

Level	# of rows
1	2
2	5
3	10
4	17
n	$n^2 + 1$

c. The differences between the number of moves it takes for each level and the number of rows in the matrix for that level are the consecutive odd numbers, beginning with one.

Level	# of moves	# of rows	Difference
1	3	2	1
2	8	5	3
3	15	10	5
4	24	17	7
n	$n^2 + 2n$	$n^2 + 1$	$2n - 1$

d. The differences between the number of resting positions and the number of rows are the consecutive even numbers, beginning with two.

Level	# of resting positions	# of rows	Difference
1	4	2	2
2	9	5	4
3	16	10	6
4	25	17	8
n	$(n + 1)^2$	$n^2 + 1$	$2n$

e. Assuming that the quadrants are numbered like those in the coordinate plane, quadrants one and three are mirror images of each other, and quadrants two and four are mirror images of each other. In the matrices with an even number of lines (levels one and three) the rows are divided evenly by a line in between two rows. In the matrices with an odd number of lines (levels two and four), the row exactly in the middle is a mirror image of itself, and can be seen as the dividing line between the upper and lower quadrants.

122

Sides and Jumps

Part 1

Instructions

At each level of the puzzle, place an equal number of markers at each end of the row, leaving one empty space in the middle. For example, in Level 1, you might place a red marker in the left space and a green one in the right. The object of the puzzle is to have the markers exchange places. The markers on the right can move to the left by sliding into an adjacent empty space or by jumping over one marker (of either color) into an empty space. The markers on the left move in the same fashion but in the opposite direction. Each color can move in one direction only, markers cannot go backwards. Write the color of the marker(s) that you put on each side in the space provided.

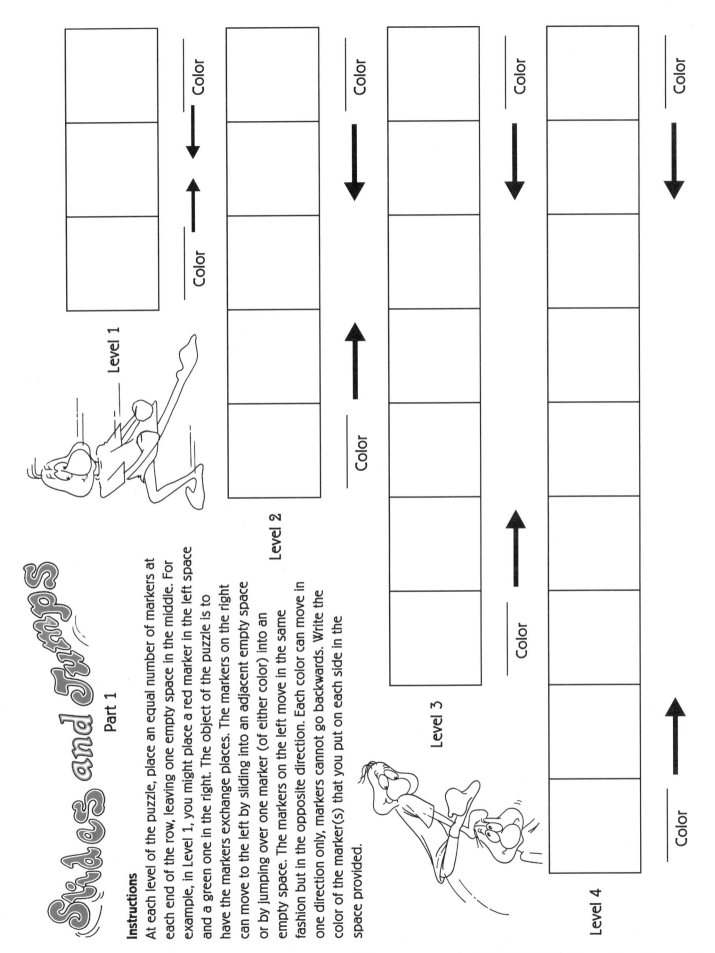

Level 1

Color ↑ ↓ Color

Level 2

Color ↓

Color ↑

Level 3

Color ↓

Color ↑

Level 4

Color ↓

Color ↑

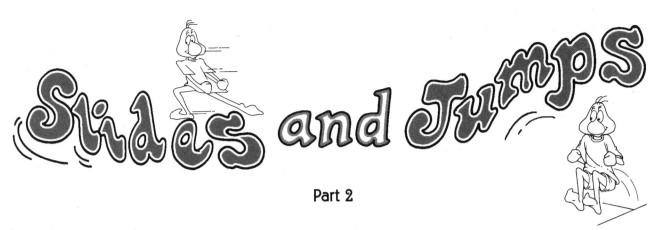

Part 2

Now that you have solved the puzzle, you can begin to look for the many patterns which exist in the solutions. Use the questions below to guide your thinking, but don't be limited by them.

1. What is the relationship between the number of markers and the number of boxes on each level? ... the number of markers and the number of the level?

2. What patterns do you notice when you look at the number of moves the markers make in each direction? (Compare numbers between levels.)

3. What is the relationship between the number of slides or jumps made by the markers and the number of the level?

4. What do you notice about the total number of moves it takes to do each level?

5. Write down any other patterns you notice in this puzzle.

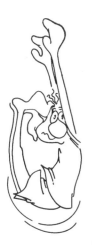

Slides and Jumps

Part 2

Now that you have solved the puzzle, you can begin to search for patterns in the solutions. For example, did you notice anything about the number of markers and the number of boxes on each level? Record as many patterns as you can discover in the space below, then share your findings with the rest of the class.

The AIMS Program

AIMS is the acronym for "Activities Integrating Mathematics and Science." Such integration enriches learning and makes it meaningful and holistic. AIMS began as a project of Fresno Pacific University to integrate the study of mathematics and science in grades K-9, but has since expanded to include language arts, social studies, and other disciplines.

AIMS is a continuing program of the non-profit AIMS Education Foundation. It had its inception in a National Science Foundation funded program whose purpose was to explore the effectiveness of integrating mathematics and science. The project directors in cooperation with 80 elementary classroom teachers devoted two years to a thorough field-testing of the results and implications of integration.

The approach met with such positive results that the decision was made to launch a program to create instructional materials incorporating this concept. Despite the fact that thoughtful educators have long recommended an integrative approach, very little appropriate material was available in 1981 when the project began. A series of writing projects have ensued and today the AIMS Education Foundation is committed to continue the creation of new integrated activities on a permanent basis.

The AIMS program is funded through the sale of this developing series of books and proceeds from the Foundation's endowment. All net income from program and products flows into a trust fund administered by the AIMS Education Foundation. Use of these funds is restricted to support of research, development, and publication of new materials. Writers donate all their rights to the Foundation to support its on-going program. No royalties are paid to the writers.

The rationale for integration lies in the fact that science, mathematics, language arts, social studies, etc., are integrally interwoven in the real world from which it follows that they should be similarly treated in the classroom where we are preparing students to live in that world. Teachers who use the AIMS program give enthusiastic endorsement to the effectiveness of this approach.

Science encompasses the art of questioning, investigating, hypothesizing, discovering, and communicating. Mathematics is a language that provides clarity, objectivity, and understanding. The language arts provide us powerful tools of communication. Many of the major contemporary societal issues stem from advancements in science and must be studied in the context of the social sciences. Therefore, it is timely that all of us take seriously a more holistic mode of educating our students. This goal motivates all who are associated with the AIMS Program. We invite you to join us in this effort.

Meaningful integration of knowledge is a major recommendation coming from the nation's professional science and mathematics associations. The American Association for the Advancement of Science in *Science for All Americans* strongly recommends the integration of mathematics, science, and technology. The National Council of Teachers of Mathematics places strong emphasis on applications of mathematics such as are found in science investigations. AIMS is fully aligned with these recommendations.

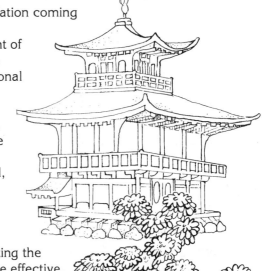

Extensive field testing of AIMS investigations confirms these beneficial results.

1. Mathematics becomes more meaningful, hence more useful, when it is applied to situations that interest students.
2. The extent to which science is studied and understood is increased, with a significant economy of time, when mathematics and science are integrated.
3. There is improved quality of learning and retention, supporting the thesis that learning which is meaningful and relevant is more effective.
4. Motivation and involvement are increased dramatically as students investigate real-world situations and participate actively in the process.

We invite you to become part of this classroom teacher movement by using an integrated approach to learning and sharing any suggestions you may have. The AIMS Program welcomes you!

AIMS Education Foundation Programs

A Day with AIMS®

Intensive one-day workshops are offered to introduce educators to the philosophy and rationale of AIMS. Participants will discuss the methodology of AIMS and the strategies by which AIMS principles may be incorporated into curriculum. Each participant will take part in a variety of hands-on AIMS investigations to gain an understanding of such aspects as the scientific/ mathematical content, classroom management, and connections with other curricular areas. *A Day with AIMS®* workshops may be offered anywhere in the United States. Necessary supplies and take-home materials are usually included in the enrollment fee.

A Week with AIMS®

Throughout the nation, AIMS offers many one-week workshops each year, usually in the summer. Each workshop lasts five days and includes at least 30 hours of AIMS hands-on instruction. Participants are grouped according to the grade level(s) in which they are interested. Instructors are members of the AIMS Instructional Leadership Network. Supplies for the activities and a generous supply of take-home materials are included in the enrollment fee. Sites are selected on the basis of applications submitted by educational organizations. If chosen to host a workshop, the host agency agrees to provide specified facilities and cooperate in the promotion of the workshop. The AIMS Education Foundation supplies workshop materials as well as the travel, housing, and meals for instructors.

AIMS One-Week Perspectives Workshops

Each summer, Fresno Pacific University offers AIMS one-week workshops on its campus in Fresno, California. AIMS Program Directors and highly qualified members of the AIMS National Leadership Network serve as instructors.

The AIMS Instructional Leadership Program

This is an AIMS staff-development program seeking to prepare facilitators for leadership roles in science/ math education in their home districts or regions. Upon successful completion of the program, trained facilitators may become members of the AIMS Instructional Leadership Network, qualified to conduct AIMS workshops, teach AIMS in-service courses for college credit, and serve as AIMS consultants. Intensive training is provided in mathematics, science, process and thinking skills, workshop management, and other relevant topics.

College Credit and Grants

Those who participate in workshops may often qualify for college credit. If the workshop takes place on the campus of Fresno Pacific University, that institution may grant appropriate credit. If the workshop takes place off-campus, arrangements can sometimes be made for credit to be granted by another institution. In addition, the applicant's home school district is often willing to grant in-service or professional-development credit. Many educators who participate in AIMS workshops are recipients of various types of educational grants, either local or national. Nationally known foundations and funding agencies have long recognized the value of AIMS mathematics and science workshops to educators. The AIMS Education Foundation encourages educators interested in attending or hosting workshops to explore the possibilities suggested above. Although the Foundation strongly supports such interest, it reminds applicants that they have the primary responsibility for fulfilling *current* requirements.

For current information regarding the programs described above, please complete the following:

Information Request

Please send current information on the items checked:

___ *Basic Information Packet* on AIMS materials   ___ *A Week with AIMS®* workshops
___ *AIMS Instructional Leadership Program*   ___ Hosting information for *A Day with AIMS®* workshops
___ *AIMS One-Week Perspectives* workshops   ___ Hosting information for *A Week with AIMS®* workshops

Name _____ Phone _____

Address _____
        Street   City   State   Zip

We invite you to subscribe to AIMS®!

Each issue of *AIMS*® contains a variety of material useful to educators at all grade levels. Feature articles of lasting value deal with topics such as mathematical or science concepts, curriculum, assessment, the teaching of process skills, and historical background. Several of the latest AIMS math/science investigations are always included, along with their reproducible activity sheets. As needs direct and space allows, various issues contain news of current developments, such as workshop schedules, activities of the AIMS Instructional Leadership Network, and announcements of upcoming publications.

AIMS® is published monthly, August through May. Subscriptions are on an annual basis only. A subscription entered at any time will begin with the next issue, but will also include the previous issues of that volume. Readers have preferred this arrangement because articles and activities within an annual volume are often interrelated.

Please note that an *AIMS*® subscription automatically includes duplication rights for one school site for all issues included in the subscription. Many schools build cost-effective library resources with their subscriptions.

YES! I am interested in subscribing to *AIMS*®.

Name _____   Home Phone _____

Address _____   City, State, Zip _____

Please send the following volumes (subject to availability):

_____	Volume VI	(1991-92)	$30.00	_____	Volume XI	(1996-97)	$30.00
_____	Volume VII	(1992-93)	$30.00	_____	Volume XII	(1997-98)	$30.00
_____	Volume VIII	(1993-94)	$30.00	_____	Volume XIII	(1998-99)	$30.00
_____	Volume IX	(1994-95)	$30.00	_____	Volume XIV	(1999-00)	$30.00
_____	Volume X	(1995-96)	$30.00	_____	Volume XV	(2000-01)	$30.00

_____ **Limited offer: Volumes XIV & XV (1999-2001) $55.00**

(Note: Prices may change without notice)

Check your method of payment:

❏ Check enclosed in the amount of $ _____

❏ Purchase order attached (Please include the P.O.#, the authorizing signature, and position of the authorizing person.)

❏ Credit Card   ❏ Visa   ❏ MasterCard   Amount $ _____

Card # _____   Expiration Date _____

Signature _____   Today's Date _____

Make checks payable to **AIMS Education Foundation.**
Mail to *AIMS*® Magazine, P.O. Box 8120, Fresno, CA 93747-8120.
Phone (559) 255-4094 or (888) 733-2467   FAX (559) 255-6396
AIMS Homepage: http://www.AIMSedu.org/

AIMS Program Publications

GRADES K-4 SERIES

Bats Incredible!
Brinca de Alegría Hacia la Primavera con las Matemáticas y Ciencias
Cáete de Gusto Hacia el Otoño con la Matemáticas y Ciencias
Cycles of Knowing and Growing
Fall Into Math and Science
Field Detectives
Glide Into Winter With Math and Science
Hardhatting in a Geo-World (Revised Edition, 1996)
Jaw Breakers and Heart Thumpers (Revised Edition, 1995)
Los Cincos Sentidos
Overhead and Underfoot (Revised Edition, 1994)
Patine al Invierno con Matemáticas y Ciencias
Popping With Power (Revised Edition, 1996)
Primariamente Física (Revised Edition, 1994)
Primarily Earth
Primariamente Plantas
Primarily Physics (Revised Edition, 1994)
Primarily Plants
Sense-able Science
Spring Into Math and Science
Under Construction

GRADES K-6 SERIES

Budding Botanist
Critters
El Botanista Principiante
Exploring Environments
Fabulous Fractions
Mostly Magnets
Ositos Nada Más
Primarily Bears
Principalmente Imanes
Water Precious Water

GRADES 5-9 SERIES

Actions with Fractions
Brick Layers
Brick Layers II
Conexiones Eléctricas
Down to Earth
Electrical Connections
Finding Your Bearings (Revised Edition, 1996)
Floaters and Sinkers (Revised Edition, 1995)
From Head to Toe
Fun With Foods
Gravity Rules!
Historical Connections in Mathematics, Volume I
Historical Connections in Mathematics, Volume II
Historical Connections in Mathematics, Volume III
Just for the Fun of It!
Machine Shop
Magnificent Microworld Adventures
Math + Science, A Solution
Off the Wall Science: A Poster Series Revisited
Our Wonderful World
Out of This World (Revised Edition, 1994)
Paper Square Geometry: The Mathematics of Origami
Pieces and Patterns, A Patchwork in Math and Science
Piezas y Diseños, un Mosaic de Matemáticas y Ciencias
Proportional Reasoning
Ray's Reflections
Soap Films and Bubbles
Spatial Visualization
The Sky's the Limit (Revised Edition, 1994)
The Amazing Circle, Volume 1
Through the Eyes of the Explorers:
   Minds-on Math & Mapping
What's Next, Volume 1
What's Next, Volume 2
What's Next, Volume 3

For further information write to:

AIMS Education Foundation • P.O. Box 8120 • Fresno, California 93747-8120
www.AIMSedu.org/ • Fax 559•255•6396